Spring Harvest
Praise
2002

Copyright and photocopying

Acknowledgements

Scripture quotations taken from the HOLY BIBLE, NEW INTERNATIONAL VERSION.
Copyright ©1973, 1978, 1984 by International Bible Society. Used by permission of Hodder and Stoughton Limited. All rights reserved. "NIV" is a registered trade mark of International Bible Society. UK trademark number 1448790

Music layout, design & type setting by David Ball, davidoxon@aol.com
Cover design by Adept Design
Printed in England by Halcyon

Spring Harvest wishes to acknowledge and thank the following people for their help in the compilation and production of this songbook: Andrew Crookall, Geraldine Latty, Deborah Lugg, Belinda Patrick, David Peacock, Sue Rinaldi, Adrian Thompson, Cheryl Williams and Spring Harvest Head Office staff. Thank you to Marie Birkinshaw, Mark Earey, Brian Hillson, Graham Kendrick, Rachael Orrell, Sue Rinaldi, Paul Sheppy, Joy Townhill, Northumbria Community Trust and Fiona Williamson for liturgy and worship tips.

ISBN 1 899 78840 9

Contents

Songs are listed in order of first line, not
title. In a few cases, alphabetical ordering
of songs has been changed slightly, in
order to ensure that page turns are not
needed in any two-page songs.

Index

Song titles differing from first lines are in italics

1

A refuge for the poor
(This is our God)

With awe
Capo 1(E)

Chris Tomlin
& Jesse Reeves

1. A re - fuge for the poor, a shel - ter from the storm: this is our God. He will wipe a - way your tears and re - turn your was - ted years: this is our God.

2. A Fa - ther to the or - phan, a heal - er to the bro - ken: this is our God. He brings peace to our mad - ness and com - fort in our sad - ness: this is our God. Oh,

3. A foun - tain for the thir - sty, a lo - ver for the lone - ly: this is our God. He brings glo - ry to the hum - ble and crowns for the faith - ful: this is our God.

mmm, this is our God. Oh,

2

All creation cries to you
(God is great)

Strongly

Marty Sampson

1. All cre - a - tion cries to you,
2. All cre - a - tion gives you praise,
3. All to you, O God we bring.

wor - ship - ping in spi - rit and in truth.
you a - lone are tru - ly great,
Je - sus teach us how to live.

Glo - ry to the Faith - ful One,
you a - lone are God who reigns
Let your fi - re burn in us that

(v.3)

all may hear, and all may see.

Je - sus Christ, God's Son.
for e - ter - ni - ty.

ry of__ your name,_____ the glo - ry of__ your name.__

2a   Proclamation of Trust

Call: We believe and trust in God the Father,
the creator and sustainer of all things

Response: **We believe and trust in Him**

Call: We believe and trust in His Son Jesus Christ,
the Saviour who redeemed the world

Response: **We believe and trust in Him**

Call: We believe and trust in the Holy Spirit,
who gives life to the people of God

Response: **We believe and trust in Him**

Call: This is our faith.

Response: **We believe and trust in one God,
Father, Son and Holy Spirit. Amen.**

3

All my days
(Beautiful Saviour)

Stuart Townend

Steadily
Capo 3(D)

1. All my days I will sing this song of glad-ness, give my
2. I will trust in the cross of my Re-dee-mer, I will
(3.) long to be where the praise is ne-ver end-ing, yearn to

praise to the Foun-tain of de-lights; for in my help-less-ness you
sing of the blood that ne-ver fails, of sins for-giv-en, of
dwell where the glo-ry ne-ver fades, where count-less wor-ship-pers will

heard my cry, and waves of mer-cy poured down on my
con-science cleansed, of death de-fea-ted and life with-out
share one song, and cries of 'wor-thy' will ho-nour the

life.
end.
Lamb!

Beau-ti-ful Sa-viour, won-der-ful

All of me

4

Worshipfully

Gareth Robinson

This song is recorded on the Spring Harvest 2002 Praise Mix Album

14

I will praise you in thought — and word and deed, — pow'r'd by — your life in me. — All of my — days, — in ev-'ry way — I will praise you, Lord.

4a   A prayer of Commitment

In darkness and in light,
in trouble and in joy,
help us, heavenly Father,
to trust your love,
to serve your purpose,
and to praise your name,
through Jesus Christ our Lord. Amen.

From *Patterns for Worship*.

5 All who are thirsty

6

Alleluia, alleluia

Moderately

Tony Ryce-Kelly
& Rónán Johnston

This song is recorded on the Spring Harvest 2002 New Songs Album

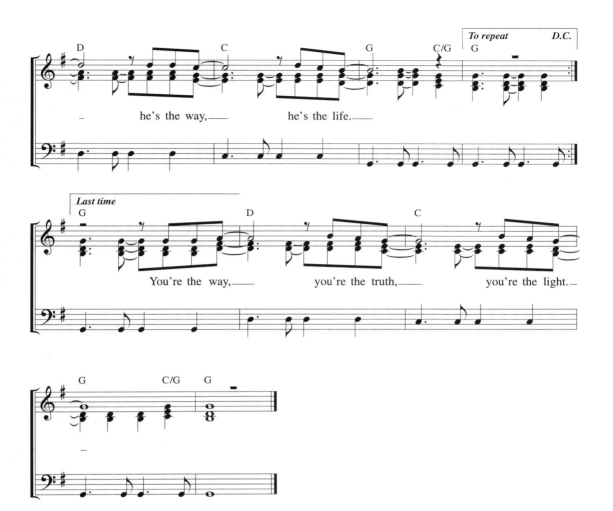

he's the way,____ he's the life.____

You're the way,____ you're the truth,____ you're the light.____

6a   Future Glory

From 1 Corinthians 2: 9

No eye has seen what God has prepared for those who love him
but God has revealed it to us by his Spirit.

No ear has heard what God has prepared for those who love him
but God has revealed it to us by his Spirit.

No mind has conceived what God has prepared for those who love him
but God has revealed it to us by his Spirit.

For we have the mind of Christ

Joy Townhill

7

As I look into your word
(Tell me of the cross)

Sheree Kima
& Johnny Markin

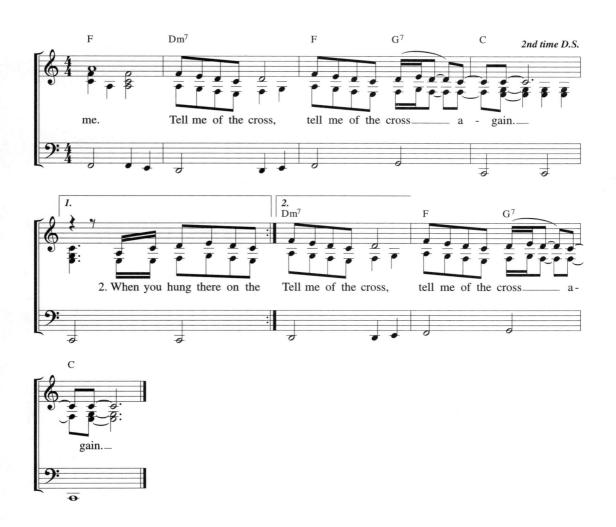

7a   Calling on God

Lord, speak to us
that we may hear your word.
Move among us
that we may behold your glory.
Receive our prayers
that we may learn to trust you.
Amen.

8   As we come to your throne

Capo 3 (D)

Andrew Grinnell

♩ = 118

This song is recorded on the Spring Harvest 2002 Praise Mix Album

23

9

As we come today
(Holy moment)

Steadily

Matt Redman

This song is recorded on the Spring Harvest 2001 Praise Mix Album

10 As we lift our voice
(Faithful God)

Jamie Hill

Bridges to C

11 At the foot of the cross

Tré Sheppard

Thoughtfully

This song is recorded on the Spring Harvest 2002 New Songs Album

11a   Eucharistic Prayer – opening dialogue

The Lord be with you.
And also with you.

Lift up your hearts.
We lift them to the Lord.

Let us give thanks to the Lord our God.
It is right to give our thanks and praise.

12

Awake, awake, O Zion
(Our God reigns)

Nathan Fellingham

13 Be thou my vision

Words: Tr. Mary Elizabeth Byrne (1880-1931)
& Eleanor Henrietta Hull (1860-1935)
Music: Ancient Irish melody

Quietly, building with strength

1. Be thou my vision, O Lord of my heart.
2. Be thou my wisdom, be thou my true word,
3. Be thou my breastplate, my sword for the fight,
4. Riches I heed not, nor man's empty praise,
5. O high King of heaven, when battle is done

Nought be all else to me, save that thou art.
I ever with thee, and thou with me, Lord.
be thou my armour and be thou my might.
thou my inheritance now and always.
grant heaven's joy to me, bright heaven's sun.

Thou my best thought in the day and the night,
Thou my great Father and I thy true son,
Be my soul's shelter, and thou my high tower,
Thou and thou only, the first in my heart,
Christ of my own heart, whatever befall,

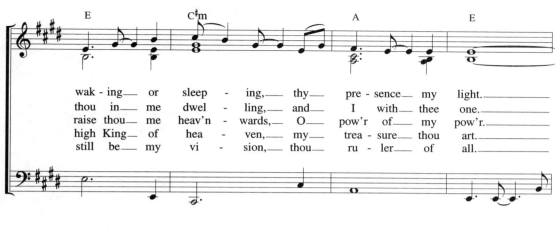

wak - ing___ or sleep - ing,___ thy___ pre - sence___ my light._____
thou in___ me dwel - ling,___ and___ I with___ thee one._____
raise thou___ me heav'n - wards,___ O___ pow'r of___ my pow'r._____
high King___ of hea - ven, my___ trea - sure___ thou art._____
still be___ my vi - sion,___ thou___ ru - ler___ of all._____

13a   Christ as a Light

Christ, as a light illumine and guide me.
Christ, as a shield over shadow me.
Christ under me; Christ over me;
Christ beside me on my left and my right.
This day be within and without me,
lowly and meek, yet all-powerful.
Be in the heart of each to whom I speak;
in the mouth of each who speaks unto me,
This day be within and without me.
lowly and meek, yet all-powerful.
Christ as a light; Christ as a shield;
Christ beside me on my left and my right.

Words by John Michael Talbot (used in Morning Office from Celtic Daily Prayer)
© Northumbria Community Trust Ltd

14 Before the throne

Majestically

Music: Vikki Cook
Words: Charite Lees Bancroft

1. Be-fore the throne of God a-bove I have a strong, a per-fect
2. When Sa-tan tempts me to de-spair and tells me of the guilt with-
3. Be-hold him there! The ri-sen Lamb, my per-fect, sin-less right-eous-

plea: a great high priest, whose name is Love, who ev-er lives and pleads for
in, up-ward I look, and see him there who made an end of all my
ness, the great un-change-a-ble 'I Am', the King of glo-ry and of

me. My name is writ-ten on his hands, my name is hid-den in his
sin. Be-cause the sin-less Sa-viour died, my sin-ful soul is count-ed
grace! One with my Lord I can-not die: my soul is pur-chased by his

heart; I know that while in heaven he stands no power can force me to de-
free; for God, the just, is sa-tis-fied to look on him and par-don
blood, my life is safe with Christ on high, with Christ, my Sa-viour and my

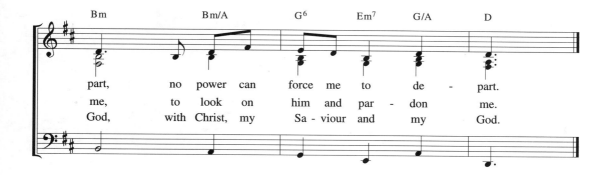

| Bm | Bm/A | G⁶ | Em⁷ | G/A | D |

part,   no power can   force me to de - part.
me,   to look on   him and par - don me.
God,   with Christ, my   Sa - viour and my God.

14a   Prayer based on Revelation 21: 3

Eternal God, dwell among us.
Save us from looking back,
lift our eyes to behold the sun of righteousness.
Light of the world, shine for ever!

Eternal God, dwell among us.
From our past call us to your future,
feed those who hunger for justice.
Bread of life, sustain us for ever!

Eternal God, dwell among us.
On our drought send your rain,
refresh those who thirst for your kingdom.
Living water, revive us for ever!

Eternal God, dwell among us.
By your word of power
free all who are snared by mistrust and suspicion.
Ground of faith, keep us true to you.

Eternal God, dwell among us.
Deliver us from despair when all seems dark,
strengthen and hearten all those who are fearful.
Hope of the ages, bring us home to you.

Paul Sheppy

15 Bless the Lord O my soul

David Hadden

15a   Let us exalt his name together

Psalm 34: 1–3

I will extol the Lord at all times;
      his praise will always be on my lips.
My soul will boast in the Lord;
      let the afflicted hear and rejoice.
Glorify the Lord with me:
      let us exalt his name together.

16

Come, let us worship

With strength

Nathan Fellingham

Verse

Come, let us wor-ship the King of kings, the Cre-
Lord, my heart and voice I raise, to

a-tor of all things. Let your soul a-rise to him, come and
praise your won-drous ways, and with con-fi-dence I come to ap-

bless the Lord our King. Come and
proach your heav'n-ly throne.

fill this place with your glo-ry, come and

17   Come, now is the time to worship

Steadily

Brian Doerksen

Still, the great-est trea-sure re-mains___ for those___ who glad - ly choose___ you now.__

17a   Invitation Liturgy

Come to Me and I will bless you says the Lord...
Draw near to Me and I will draw near to you...
If you come with us we will share with you all the good things...
that the Lord has done among us and for us...
Come to Me for I have heard you calling in the night...
Come, everyone who is thirsty, here is water!...
Come, you who have no money, come and feast!...
Come back, return to Me My people,
       come home to the place of your belonging...
Come, and I will teach you...
Come in and share My joy...
Let the children come and do not stop them...
Come all of you who are tired and weary...

I will come and take you to be where I am...
Come...

18

Come praise our God

Graham Kendrick

Come praise our God, all you his servants, all you who fear him. Both small and great come on and praise him, the Lord, the Al-mighty. mighty. Hallelujah, hallelujah, our Lord God Almighty reigns. Halelu mighty reigns.

Let us re-joice and be glad, and give him glo - ry! For the
Fine li - nen, bright and clean to her was gi - ven. It's the

wed-ding of the Lamb has come, his bride has made her-self rea - dy.
right-eous deeds of all the saints, it's time we made our-selves

rea - dy. Hal - le - lu -

18a Worshipping in spirit and truth

From John 4: 24

God is Spirit.
Let us worship him in spirit and truth.
The Lord is with us.
Let us praise his name together.

19

Come, see the Lord
in his breathtaking splendour

BARNARD GATE

Words: Martin E. Leckebusch
Music: John Barnard

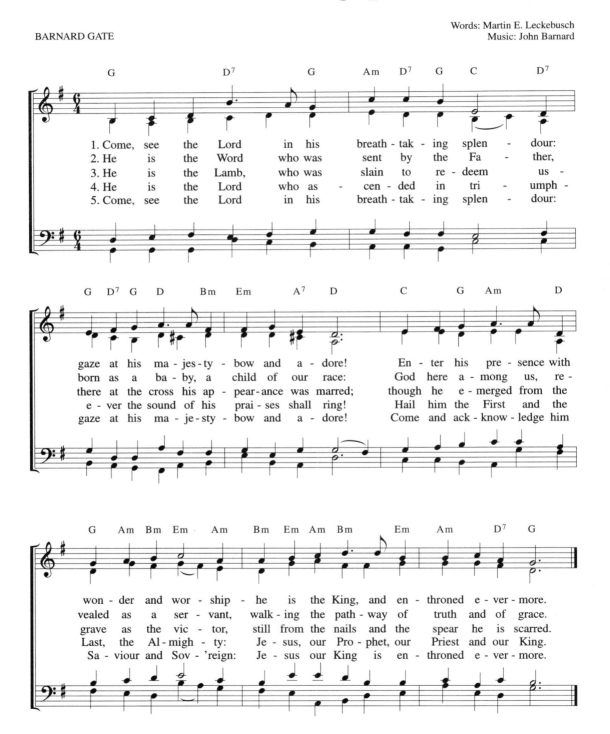

1. Come, see the Lord in his breath-tak-ing splen-dour:
2. He is the Word who was sent by the Fa-ther,
3. He is the Lamb, who was slain to re-deem us—
4. He is the Lord who as-cen-ded in tri-umph—
5. Come, see the Lord in his breath-tak-ing splen-dour:

gaze at his ma-jes-ty—bow and a-dore! En-ter his pre-sence with
born as a ba-by, a child of our race: God here a-mong us, re-
there at the cross his ap-pear-ance was marred; though he e-merged from the
e-ver the sound of his prai-ses shall ring! Hail him the First and the
gaze at his ma-je-sty-bow and a-dore! Come and ack-now-ledge him

won-der and wor-ship—he is the King, and en-throned e-ver-more.
vealed as a ser-vant, walk-ing the path-way of truth and of grace.
grave as the vic-tor, still from the nails and the spear he is scarred.
Last, the Al-migh-ty: Je-sus, our Pro-phet, our Priest and our King.
Sa-viour and Sov-'reign: Je-sus our King is en-throned e-ver-more.

Don't be afraid

Gently

John L. Bell

Don't be a-fraid. My love is strong-er, my love is strong-er than your

fear. Don't be a-fraid. My love is strong-er and

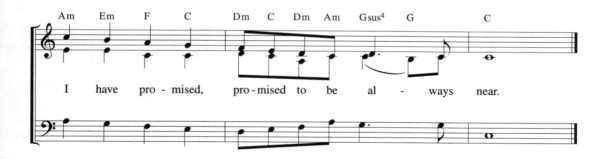

I have pro-mised, pro-mised to be al — ways near.

20a   Do not be afraid

Deuteronomy 31: 6

Be strong and courageous.
Do not be afraid or terrified because of them,
for the Lord your God goes with you;
he will never leave you nor forsake you.

21 Do in my life

Tony Hiebert
& Christian Stonehouse

Am Am7/G D/F♯ Em Em7/D C G/B
de - part from me, I need you more than words can
the heart you seek, let me bring ho - nour to your
1. Am G/B C2 D
2. Am G/B C2 D G
D.C.
say. name to - day. Do in my life
Coda
G/B Em Am D7
1.,2. G
3. G
do in me what on - ly you can do. Just

21a The Lord's Prayer

Our Father in heaven,
hallowed be your name,
your kingdom come,
your will be done
on earth as in heaven.
Give us today our daily bread.
Forgive us our sins,
as we forgive those who sin against us.
Lead us not into temptation,
but deliver us from evil,
for the kingdom, the power and the glory are yours,
now and forever, Amen.

Text of Lord's Prayer from ASB 1980 © Archbishops' Council of the Church of England.

22   Draw me close to you

Kelly Carpenter

(continued over...)

help me know you are near.

Help me know you are here.

22a   **Confession**

You know my thoughts from afar, O Lord.
You search out my path and my lying down.
You are acquainted with all my ways.
[Silence]
Have mercy Lord.
Cleanse me from my sin.

23 Drawn from every tribe

Revelation 7

Steadily
Capo 1(D)

David Lyle Morris
& Faith Forster

1. Drawn from e-v'ry tribe, e-v'ry tongue and na-tion,
2. We are those who fol-low, through scenes of fie-ry trial,
3. Ne-ver will we hun-ger, we'll no lon-ger thirst, there's

ga-thered be-fore the throne. Cast-ing down their crowns, they
draw-ing from wells of grace. Through the dark-est val-ley
shade from the heat of day. Led to springs of life,

fall at his feet and wor-ship the Lord a-lone.
from the depths of pain, we'll come to that ho-ly place.
Je-sus, our Shep-herd, will wipe e-v'ry tear a-way. Our

What a glo-rious sight, dressed in robes of white,
We will o-ver-come by look-ing to the Lamb and
God up-on the throne will shel-ter all his own who

(continued over...)

23a   Jesus Christ is King of kings

From Colossians 1

Leader:	Jesus Christ is King of kings
All:	**Yes he is! Yes he is!**
Leader:	He's the reason that we sing
All:	**Yes he is! Yes he is!**
Leader:	He created heaven and earth
All:	**Yes he did! Yes he did!**
Leader:	And he is Lord over the church
All:	**Yes he is! Yes he is!**
Leader:	Jesus Christ is the Lord of lords
All:	**Yes he is! Yes he is!**
Leader:	And now he is our special friend
All:	**Yes he is! Yes he is!**
Leader:	Lord help us as we pray today
All:	**Help us Lord! Help us Lord!**
Leader:	That we'll continue in your way
All:	**That we'll continue in your way!**

All: **To the Father and the Son and the Holy Spirit too**
                be the honour be the praise, our Lord God we worship you!

Encourage people to walk on the spot as they say the words. Adding percussion instruments and handclaps may help secure the rhythm.
The last verse could have hands gradually raised to end in a last shout of praise 'We worship you'.

Geraldine Latty

24 Empty, broken, here I stand
(Kyrie eleison)

Nick & Anita Haigh

25 Father we bow at the cross

Tom Callister
& Daniel Bowring

Capo 2 (A)

Father,—— we bow at the—— cross,—— know-ing the

cost you've paid o-pens the way to— life with— you. Thank-you

Lord, for the grace to live a-gain,—— your ho-ly

name we'll— sing— as praise to our ri-sen King.—— You are—

Chorus B(A)   G#m(F#m)

(Maintain 6/8 feel)

Lord in this place, you are— Lord in this place, and

C#m(Bm)   B/D#(A)   *1.* F#m(Em)   E(D)

no o-ther name— will be lift-ed high-er than Je - sus. You are—

2. F#m(Em)   E(D)   B(A)

Je - sus.—

25a   Response prayer for peace

Leader: Come, Lord Jesus. Come, Lord Jesus.
Response: **Still our restless souls.**
Leader: Come, Lord Jesus. Come, Lord Jesus.
Response: **Come and make us whole.**
Leader: Come, Lord Jesus. Please come, Lord Jesus.
Response: **Come now to give us your peace.**
All: **Amen**

26

From the squalor
(Immanuel)

With a 'celtic' feel

Stuart Townend

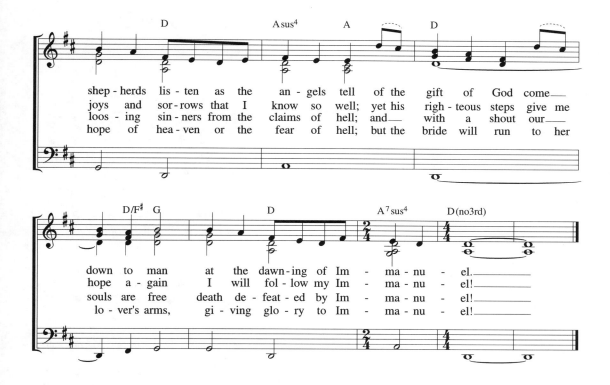

shep - herds lis - ten as the an - gels tell of the gift of God come—
joys and sor - rows that I know so well; yet his righ - teous steps give me
loos - ing sin - ners from the claims of hell; and— with a shout our—
hope of hea - ven or the fear of hell; but the bride will run to her

down to man at the dawn - ing of Im - ma - nu - el.—
hope a - gain I will fol - low my Im - ma - nu - el!—
souls are free death de - feat - ed by Im - ma - nu - el!—
lo - ver's arms, gi - ving glo - ry to Im - ma - nu - el!—

26a   The Apostles creed

I believe in God, the Father almighty,
creator of heaven and earth.
I believe in Jesus Christ, his only Son, our Lord.
He was conceived by the power of the Holy Spirit
and born of the Virgin Mary.
He suffered under Pontius Pilate,
was crucified, died and was buried.
On the third day he rose again.
He ascended into heaven,
and is seated at the right hand of the Father.
He will come again to judge the living and the dead.
I believe in the Holy Spirit, the holy catholic Church,
the communion of the saints, the forgiveness of sins,
the resurrection of the body, and the life everlasting.
Amen.

27 Give me one pure and holy passion

Steadily

Mark Altrogge

Give me one pure and ho-ly pas-sion, give me one mag-ni-fi-cent ob-ses-sion. Je-sus, give me one glo-ri-ous am-bi-tion for my life to know and fol-low hard af-ter you. To know and fol-low hard af-ter you, to

grow as your— di-sci - ple in— the truth.— This world is emp-ty, pale and poor— com-pared to know-ing you,— my Lord;— lead me on— and I will run af - ter you.—

27a   Knowing Christ

Philippians 3: 10–11

I want to know Christ and the power of his resurrection
and the fellowship of sharing in his sufferings,
becoming like him in his death, and so, somehow,
to attain to the resurrection from the dead.

28

Give thanks to the Lord
(Forever)

Chris Tomlin

Moderato

This song is recorded on the Spring Harvest 2002 New Songs Album

29

God of the mountains
(Creation praise)

Moderately

Sue Rinaldi,
Caroline Bonnett & Steve Bassett

1. God of the moun-tains, God of the
2. Wis-dom of a - ges, light in the

— sea, God of the hea-vens,
— dark, home for the out-cast,

of e - ter - ni - ty. God of the
peace for the heart: friend of the

fu - ture, God of the past,
lone - ly, strength for op - pressed,

This song is recorded on the Spring Harvest 2001 Live Worship Album

God of — the pre - sent, — God of all hi - sto - ry. — Cre -
voice of — the voice - less, — God of all li - ber - ty. —

Chorus

a - tion praise — will thun - der — to — you, thun - der — to — you,

thun - der — to — you. Cre - a - tion — praise — will thun - der — to — you, I'm

lost in — the won - der, lost in — the won - der — of — you.

30 Good and gracious

Gareth Robinson

Steadily

1. Good and gra - cious, att - ri - butes of a lo - ving Fath - er, you're high and migh - ty, but hum - ble all the same. You have made the hea - vens and the earth, and you made us in your im - age, Lord. Ho - ly,

2. Death and hell are now no lon - ger things I fear be - cause you have saved me and I'm grate - ful to the core. I'm your child be - cause of Je - sus' blood, and your Spi - rit leads me, guides me, fills me.

This song is recorded on the Spring Harvest 2002 Praise Mix Album

(continued over...)

love, your grace, your joy, your peace and more.

Ho - ly, ho - ly.

D.S. al fine

30a   Christ the Beginning and the End

From Revelation 1: 5, 6 & 8

Alpha and Omega:
first and last.
Who was, and is;
who is to come.

Jesus was the first to conquer death.
He reigns over all earthly rulers.
Christ has shown his love for us.
By his blood he set us free.
He shares his reign and calls us to serve.
To him be glory and power for ever!

Alpha and Omega:
first and last.
Who was, and is;
who is to come.

31 Great and marvellous

Rev 15: 3-4

Carey Luce
& Geraldine Latty

In a latin style ♩ = 75

1. Great and mar - vel - lous are your deeds, O God, sov'-reign o - ver all,
just and right - eous in e - v'ry way. Great King for all time

2. Great and mar - vel - lous are your deeds, O Lord, how we long to see
your plan in our time re - vealed: hearts long - ing to wor -

(continued over...)

70

this place,— thank-ing you— for sav - ing grace,—

bur-dens rolled— to Cal - va-ry,— once in chains— but— now set— free.

31a　　Jesus

Based on Colossians 1: 15

We cannot see God
but Jesus is just like him in every detail.

Before there was anything -
before rocks, the sky, oxygen, atoms
or anything we call 'matter'
Jesus ruled

When there was only darkness and chaos
he knew my name
Jesus loves

To reconcile all things,
both on earth and in heaven
Jesus died

He is in control of all things
Jesus reigns

Joy Townhill

32

Great is the darkness
(Come, Lord Jesus)

Growing in strength

Gerald Coates
& Noel Richards

Verse

1. Great is the dark-ness that cov-ers the earth, op-pres-sion, in-jus-tice and pain. Na-tions are slip-ping in hope-less des-pair, though ma-ny have come in your name. Watch-ing while sa-ni-ty dies, touched by the mad-ness and lies.

2. May now your church rise with po-wer and love, this glo-ri-ous go-spel pro-claim. In ev-'ry na-tion sal-va-tion will come to those who be-lieve in your name. Help us bring light to this world, that we might speed your re-turn.

3. Great ce-le-bra-tions on that fi-nal day when out of the hea-vens you come. Dark-ness will va-nish, all sor-row will end, and ru-lers will bow at your throne. Our great com-mis-sion com-plete, then face to face we shall meet.

Chorus

Come, Lord Je-sus, come, Lord Je-sus, pour out your Spi-rit we pray. Come, Lord Je-sus, come, Lord Je-sus, pour out your Spi-rit on us to-day.

32a Prayer for the Peace of the World

Almighty God,
from whom all thoughts of truth and peace proceed:
kindle, we pray, in the hearts of all, the true love of peace
and guide with your pure and peaceable wisdom
those who take counsel for the nations of the earth
that in tranquillity your kingdom may go forward,
till the earth is filled with the knowledge of your love;
through Jesus Christ your Son our Lord,
who is alive and reigns with you,
in the unity of the Holy Spirit,
one God, now and forever.

From The Book of Common Prayer

33 Great is your faithfulness

Words: Thomas Chisholm (1866-1960)
Music: William Runyan (1870-1957)

1. Great is your faith-ful-ness, O God my Fa-ther, you have ful-filled all your pro-mise to me; you ne-ver fail and your love is un-chang-ing – all you have been, you for ev-er will be.

2. Sum-mer and win-ter, and spring-time and har-vest, sun, moon and stars in their cours-es a-bove join with all na-ture in e-lo-quent wit-ness to your great faith-ful-ness, mer-cy and love.

3. Par-don for sin, and a peace e-ver-last-ing, – your liv-ing pre-sence to cheer and to guide; strength for to-day and bright hope for to-mor-row these are the bles-sings your love will pro-vide.

Chorus Great is your faith-ful-ness, great is your faith-ful-ness, morn-ing by

morn - ing new mer-cies I see; all I have need-ed your hand has pro -
vi - ded, great is your faith - ful-ness, Fa - ther, to me.

33a   A Prayer of Trust

Lord, I believe You will make a way for me
and provide for me, if only I trust You and obey.
I will trust in the darkness and know
that my times are still in Your hand.
I will believe You for my future,
chapter by chapter, until all the story is written.
Focus my mind and my heart upon You,
my attention always on You without alteration.
Strengthen me with Your blessing
and appoint to me the task.
Teach me to live with eternity in view.
Tune my spirit to the music of heaven.

From the Brendan liturgy ('In Exploration of a Vision')
Celtic Daily Prayer, © Northumbria Community Trust Ltd

34

Have we forgotten?
(Saviour and Friend)

Andy Ferrett

Have we for-got-ten the price that's been paid?
It was my life he paid with his pain,

Have we re-mem-bered the wage of our ways?
suf-fered at the hands of those he had made.

Can we dis-miss what he's done on the cross as
Can we con-si-der what he once went through to be

fool-ish-ness? Oh, thank you, oh,
with us?

This song is recorded on the Spring Harvest 2002 New Songs Album

(continued over...)

34a   God's love for the world

John 3: 16 & 17

For God so loved the world that he gave his one and only Son,
that whoever believes in him shall not perish but have eternal life.
For God did not send his Son into the world to condemn the world,
but to save the world through him.

35

He once was dead
(The First, the Last, the Living One)

David Lyle Morris
& Nick Wynne-Jones

a-lone:___ the First,___ the Last,___ the Liv - ing One.___

1. G/D D.S. | 2. D.C.

You, Lord___   3. You once___

35a   Jesus is Risen

Leader: What's that you say?
People: **Jesus is risen**
Leader: But he was dead
People: **Jesus is risen**
Leader: Nailed to a cross
People: **Jesus is risen**
Leader: Laid in a grave
People: **Jesus is risen**
Leader: dead for three days
People: **Jesus is risen**
Leader: Now he's alive?
People: **Jesus is risen**
Leader: death overcome?
People: **Jesus is risen**
Leader: [triumphantly] Hope for us all
People: **Jesus is risen**
Leader: Shout with one voice
People: **Jesus is risen! Alleluia!**

Source unknown.

36 Have you heard?
(My best friend)

Joel Houston
& Marty Sampson

Lively

1. Have you heard of the One called Sa-viour? Have you heard of his per-fect love?
2. I be-lieve in the One called Sa-viour, I be-lieve he's the ri-sen One,

Have you heard of the One in hea-ven? Have you heard how he gave his Son?
I be-lieve that I'll live for-e-ver, I be-lieve that the King will come.

'Cause I have found this love, and I be-lieve in the Son; show me your

way.

Je-sus, you are my best friend, you will al-ways be, and no-thing will e-

37 Hear my prayer, O Lord

Psalm 61

Debbie Owens

Steadily

Hear my prayer, O Lord,— from the ends— of the earth I cry.— Your peace will lead— me to— the Rock that is high - er than I.—

For you have been my strength in times— of trou - ble, a tow-er a-bove—

38   Heavenly hosts in ceaseless worship

Capo 5(C)
HYFRYDOL

Music: Rowland Hugh Prichard (1811-87)
Words: Timothy Dudley-Smith

Joyfully

1. Heav-'nly hosts in cease-less wor-ship 'ho-ly, ho-ly,
2. All cre-a-tion, all re-demp-tion, join to sing the

ho-ly!' cry; 'He who is, who was and will be,
Sa-viour's worth; Lamb of God whose blood has bought us,

God Al-migh-ty, Lord most high.' Praise and ho-nour,
kings and priests, to reign on earth. Wealth and wis-dom,

pow'r and glo-ry, be to him who reigns a-lone!
pow'r and glo-ry, ho-nour, might, do-mi-nion, praise,

We,— with all— his hands— have fa - shioned, fall be -
now— be his— from all— his crea - tures and to

fore— the Fa - ther's throne.
e - ver - last - ing days!

These words can also be sung to the hymn tune BLAENWERN (Love Divine)

38a   Worthy is the Lamb

Revelation 5: 12–13

In a loud voice they sang:

> 'Worthy is the Lamb, who was slain,
> to receive power and wealth and
>   wisdom and strength
> and honour and glory and praise!'

Then I heard every creature in heaven and on earth and under the earth and on the sea, and all that is in them, singing:

> 'To him who sits on the throne and to the Lamb
> be praise and honour and glory and power,
>   for ever and ever!'

39 Here I am and I have come
(I will always love your name)

Rhythmically

Paul Oakley

thank— you, Lord.___
thank— you, Lord.___
thank— you, Lord.___

No great-er love— was
And not by— works,— but
You're mak-ing— me— to

e - ver— shown,— no bet - ter life— e - ver was laid down.___
by your— grace— you clothe me— now— in your right-eous-ness.___
be like— you,— to do the works— of the Fa - ther, too.___

Chorus

And I_____ will al - ways love your— name;

and I_____ will al - ways sing your— praise.___

1.

And I—

2.

D.C. | *Last time only*

2. You
3. You

89

40

Here I stand, forgiven
(Find me at the cross)

Chris O'Brien

Steadily

41

Here I stand

Moderato

Words: Rev 3.20
Music: John L. Bell

Here I stand at the door and knock, and knock.

Here I stand at the door and knock, and

I will come and dine with those who ask me in.

knock. I will dine with those who ask me in.

41a   Jesus at the door

Revelation 3: 20

Here I am! I stand at the door and knock.
If anyone hears my voice and opens the door,
I will come in and eat with him, and he with me.

42 Here I wait beneath the cross

Capo 1 (D)

With quiet intensity

Tim Sherrington

Here I wait beneath the cross,
Here I come to give my all, my
rest - ing in the pre-sence of your love.
hands reach up in ho-ly praise to you.

Here I wait to know your heart, as I
Here I cast all chains a-side to

wor-ship you in spi-rit and in truth. For

(continued over...)

Je - sus, faith - ful till the end,— Je -

sus, the King of kings.——

D.C. To end

42a   Christ – God's foolish wisdom

We praise you Jesus, for the way you came to us:
not as a ruler; but loving and serving us.
This is the stumbling block – Jesus our Lord!

We praise you Jesus, for the way you died for us:
you did no wrong; yet you died on the cross for us.
This is the stumbling block – Jesus our Lord!

We praise you Jesus, for crushing the pride in us:
we could not earn what you gave as a gift to us.
This is the stumbling block – Jesus our Lord!

We praise you Jesus, for showing God's plan to us:
foolish to many, God's wisdom walked here with us.
This is the stumbling block – Jesus our Lord!

43 Holiness surrounds his throne
(For the love of God)

Steadily

Words: D. A. Carson
Music: Steve James

1. Ho - li - ness sur - rounds his throne; all his an - gels— bow. Sheer de - light is theirs a - lone,— wor - ship - ping him now. Jus - tice tri - umphs, beau - ty— reigns, no - thing marred or— flawed; count - less mil - lions join in

2. God so loved this sin - cursed world that he gave his— Son; Jes - us is God's love un - furled,— else I'd be un - done. Con - tem - plat - ing such a— love, I am hum - bled,— awed. I in turn pro - claim good

3. Heart and soul and strength and mind: would that I were— true. Faith - ful - ly a - dor - ing him,— ut - ter - ly re - newed! How I long to of - fer— him pure love, not a— fraud; still, I raise my halt - ing

praise,— for the love of God. Count-less mil - lions join in
news— for the love of God, I in turn pro - claim good
hymn— for the love of God. Still, I raise my halt - ing

praise,—for the love of God.
news—for the love of God.
hymn—for the love of God.

To end

43a   God the Creator

Revelation 4: 11

'You are worthy, our Lord and God,
     to receive glory and honour and power,
For you created all things,
     and by your will they were created
     and have their being.'

44

Holy fire

Steve Mitchinson
& Brian Doerksen

With a steady rock feel

1. Ho - ly fire___ from hea - ven, de - scend to us___ we pray,___ let us burn
2. Ho - ly breath___ from hea - ven, de - scend to us___ we pray,___ let us breathe___
3. Ho - ly stream___ from hea - ven, de - scend to us___ we pray,___ let us drink

___ a - gain.___ Ho - ly fire___ from hea - ven, con -
___ a - gain.___ Ho - ly breath___ from hea - ven, re -
___ a - gain.___ Ho - ly stream___ from hea - ven,

sume our hearts___ to - day,___ let us burn___ a - gain,
vive our hearts___ to - day,___ let us breathe___ a - gain,
bring new life___ to - day,___ let us drink___ a - gain,

let us burn____ a - gain.____
let us breathe____ a - gain.____
let us drink____ a - gain.____

Wait-ing in___ ex-pec-

tan-cy,____ sur-ren - dered to___ your sov - 'reign-ty,___ we're hun -

gry for___ true in - ti - ma - cy, Lord,____

for the things of your heart.____

____ a - gain,____   let us burn____ a - gain.____

99

45 Holy is your name

Andrew Grinnell

Steadily

1. Ho - ly is your name,— ho - ly is— your name,
2. How I love your name,— sweet-est name— to me,

bring - ing— peace and love,— cov - 'ring all— my
pro - claim it to the earth,— bring in li - ber -

shame. Je - sus, Je - sus,
ty.

Je - sus, Je - sus.

46 Holy Spirit we wait on you

Andrew Rayner
Arr. Richard Lewis

47 How deep the Father's love

Capo 2(D)

Stuart Townend

Thoughtfully

1. How deep the Fa-ther's love for us, how vast be-yond all mea - sure, that he should give his on - ly Son to make a wretch his trea - sure. How great the pain of sear - ing loss, the Fa - ther turns his face a -

2. Be - hold the man up - on a cross, my sin up - on his shoul - ders; a - shamed, I hear my mock-ing voice call out a - mong the scof - fers. It was my sin that held him there un - til it was ac - com -

3. I will not boast in a - ny - thing, no gifts, no pow'r, no wis - dom; but I will boast in Je - sus Christ, his death and re - sur - rec - tion. Why should I gain from his re - ward? I can - not give an an -

way, as wounds which mar the cho-sen One bring
plished; his dy-ing breath has brought me life-I
swer, but this I know with all my heart, his

ma-ny sons to glo-ry.
know that it is fin-ished.
wounds have paid my ran-som.

47a   God's love

Romans 5: 8

But God demonstrates his own love for us in this:
While we were still sinners, Christ died for us.

48   How lovely is your dwelling place

Linda Jones

Slowly

48a   One day in your courts

Psalm 84: 10

Better is one day in your courts
      than a thousand elsewhere;
I would rather be a doorkeeper in the house of my God
      than dwell in the tents of the wicked.

Hungry
(Falling on my knees)

Kathy Scott

1.,3. Hun-gry, I come to you, for I know you sa-tis-fy.
2. Bro-ken, I run to you, for your arms are o-pen wide;

I am emp-ty, but I know your love does not run dry.
I am wea-ry, but I know your touch re-stores my life.

So I wait for you, so I wait for you.

Chorus I'm fall - ing on my knees, of-fer-ing all of me.

49a   In the Right Place

My soul's desire is to see the face of God
and to rest in His house.
My soul's desire is to study the Scriptures
and to learn the ways of God.
My soul's desire is to be freed from
all fear and sadness, and to share Christ's risen life.
My soul's desire is to imitate my King,
and to sing His purposes always.
My soul's desire is to enter the gates
of heaven and to gaze upon the light
that shines forever.

Dear Lord, You alone know
what my soul truly desires,
and You alone can
satisfy those desires.

From the Hild liturgy ('In the Right Place'), Celtic Daily Prayer
© *Northumbria Community Trust Ltd*

50 I behold your power and glory
(Irresistible)

Moderately

Darlene Zschech

I be-hold your pow'r and glo-ry, bring an off - 'ring, come be-fore you; wor-ship you, Lord, in the beau-ty of your ho - li-ness. When-e-ver I call, you're there, Re-deem - er and Friend; che-rished be - yond all words, this

love ne - ver ends._____ Morn - ing by morn - ing___ your

mer - cy a - wa - kens my soul._____ I lift up my

eyes to___ see___ the won - ders of hea - ven o - pen-ing o - ver___ me,___ your

good - ness a - bounds;___ you've tak - en my breath a - way___ with your___

_ ir - re - sis - ti - ble love._____

51
I have heard
(The Father's song)

This song is recorded on the Spring Harvest 2001 New Songs Album

(continued over...)

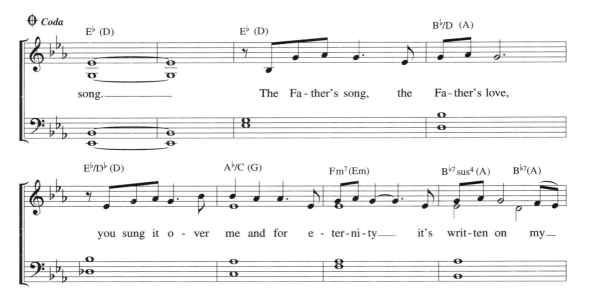

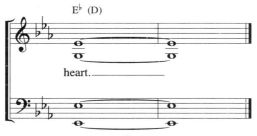

51a   The Father's song

Zephaniah 3: 17

The Lord your God is with you,
    he is mighty to save.
He will take great delight in you,
    he will quiet you with his love,
    he will rejoice over you with singing.

Using Liturgy in Worship (1)

The Spring Harvest songbook contains a feast of liturgy. It's important to think through how and where it might be used.

What is 'Liturgy'?

Liturgy comes from a Greek word and means literally 'the people's offering'.

Liturgy is public worship which is:

- Structured – though this does not mean there is no room for the spontaneous or 'Spirit led'.
- Corporate – it belongs to all of us, not just to the leader – that is why liturgy is often repeated and draws on existing words.
- Holistic – it includes actions, symbols and movement as well as words.

Sometimes people use it to mean 'spoken words' (as opposed to songs and hymns). Liturgical texts do for speaking what songs and hymns do for music: they give the congregation a part.

Some worry that liturgy can descend into the vain repetition that Jesus criticised. It can, of course – but so can using the same song or hymn lots of times. What Jesus criticised was *vain* repetition – piling up the words, thinking that God is more likely to listen – not repetition as such.

What does Liturgy do?

Liturgy (used properly) gives every one, not just one or two, a voice in public corporate worship. Singing is not the only way of worshipping as a body – and not everyone feels comfortable or competent singing in public.

Liturgical texts have several strengths:

- They can support and reinforce learning. Most liturgical texts are based on passages from Scripture. Speaking them out is a way of reinforcing the message of Scripture and 'praying in' the teaching.
- They can reinforce the gospel message of the season. The church year (Advent, Christmas etc.) developed as a way of focussing on key aspects of the gospel every year. Some of the liturgical material in the Spring Harvest songbook reflects the seasonal emphasis of Easter.
- They can provide a means of responding to God and to the teaching. This can be especially helpful when you want to encourage not only individual responses, but a corporate response.

Mark Earey
Praxis National Education Officer, Sarum College Institute for Liturgy and Mission

52

I look to the Rock
(You're my all in all)

Sam Chaplin

Laid back gospel feel

1. I look to the Rock— that is high - er than I.— I
2. Now that my life— is hid - den in Christ— the

stand in a right - eous-ness not— my— own.— Where I have failed,—
life that I live— is no lon - ger— mine.— And all that is his— is

you have pre-vailed,— and clothed— me— in your grace.— You're my
gi - ven to me— and clothes— me— in his grace.—

ev - 'ry breath,— you're my right-eous-ness,— you're my all— in all.—

You're my rest-ing place,— you're my first and last,— you're my all— in all.—

53
I'm giving you my heart
(*Surrender*)

Marc James

Slowly ♩ = 60

1. I'm giv-ing you — my heart, and all that is — with-in
2. I'm sing-ing you — this song, I'm wait-ing at — the cross,

I lay it all — down — for the sake of you, my
and all the world — holds — dear, I count it all — as —

King. — I'm giv-ing you — my dreams, I'm lay-ing down — my — rights,
— loss. For the sake of know - ing you, the glo - ry of — your — name, —

— I'm giv-ing up — my — pride for the pro-mise of — new life. And
— to know the last-ing — joy, e - ven shar-ing in — your pain.

This song is recorded on the Spring Harvest 2001 New Songs Album

Chorus

I___ sur - ren - der all to you,_____ all__ to you. And

I___ sur - ren - der all to you,_____ all__ to you.

To end

53a   Encouragement to keep going

Hebrews 12: 2–3

Let us fix our eyes on Jesus, the author and perfecter of our faith,
who for the joy set before him endured the cross, scorning its
shame, and sat down at the right hand of the throne of God.
Consider him who endured such opposition from sinful men,
so that you will not grow weary and lose heart.

54　I'm making melody in my heart to you

Matt Redman

name? How can souls not sing your

praise? Je - sus, you've put

mu - sic in my soul.

last time D.S. **To end**

rit last time.......

55

Immortal, invisible

Words: Walter Smith
Music: Welsh hymn melody
Arr. David Peacock

Reflectively

1. Im - mor - tal, in - vi - si - ble, God on - ly wise, in light in - ac -
2. Un - rest - ing, un - hast - ing, and si - lent as light, nor want - ing, nor
3. To all you are giv - ing, to both great and small, in all you are
4. We wor - ship be - fore you, great Fa - ther of light, while an - gels a -

ces - si - ble hid from our eyes; most ho - ly, most glo - rious, the
wast - ing, you rule us in might; your jus - tice like moun - tains high
liv - ing, the true life of all: we blos - som and flour - ish, un -
dore you, all veil - ing their sight; our prais - es we ren - der, O

An - cient of Days, al - migh - ty, vic - to - rious, your great name we
soar - ing a - bove, your clouds which are foun - tains of good - ness and
cer - tain and frail; we wit - her and pe - rish, but you ne - ver
Fa - ther, to you whom on - ly the splen - dour of light hides from

praise.
love.
fail.
view.

Using Liturgy in Worship (2)

How to use the liturgical texts.

The key to using liturgical texts is to see how they fit within the flow of the whole act of worship.

- Think about how you will introduce them. Where possible, warn people about texts that are coming up, or songs that will follow on from the spoken word, so that the worship itself can flow without too many interruptions for instructions.

- Be ready to use silence before and/or after spoken words. This is especially important if the words are not familiar – it allows people to take in what they are about to say or have just said.

- Make the music and spoken word flow as easily as possible into one another. Don't forget that liturgical texts can be 'inserted' into songs (vice versa), with the music continuing quietly in the background underneath the spoken words. This sort of approach can enhance both, giving the spoken words new emotional depth and the song a greater depth of content. Look for opportunities, but don't forget to give clear instructions beforehand.

- Look for a mix of format. Some liturgical material is primarily for the leader, some is balanced between leader and response, some is simple congregational prayer, some involves several voices.

- Look for a mix of style. Some liturgical texts need almost to be shouted, whereas others need a quieter and more reflective approach.

- Don't forget to think about posture. If the liturgical text needs a strong sense of corporate response or prayer, then standing may be most natural. A text which invites a more reflective or individual approach might be more appropriately said sitting or kneeling.

- Don't be afraid to use something more than once. Like songs and hymns, many liturgical texts only really come into their own when they are repeated or used often, so that they start to 'sink in' and people can concentrate on the meaning not the mechanics. Some pieces can be repeated within one act of worship (for instance, once near the beginning to set the scene and again after the teaching to allow for deeper reflection).

Mark Earey
Praxis National Education Officer, Sarum College Institute for Liturgy and Mission

56   In Christ alone

Words: Stuart Townend
Music: Keith Getty

Capo 1 (D)
Steadily

This song is recorded on the Spring Harvest 2001 Live Worship Album

peace, when fears are stilled, when striv - ings cease! My com - for-
died, the wrath of God was sa - tis - fied - for e - v'ry
ry sin's curse has lost its grip on me, for I am
man, can e - ver pluck me from his hand; till he re-

ter, my all in all, here in the love of Christ I stand.
sin on him was laid; here in the death of Christ I live.
his and he is mine - bought with the pre - cious blood of Christ.
turns or calls me home, here in the pow'r of Christ I'll stand!

56a   Nothing to fear

Psalm 27: 1

The Lord is my light and my salvation –
    whom shall I fear?
The Lord is the stronghold of my life –
    of whom shall I be afraid?

57
In every day that dawns
(I know you love me)

Kate Simmonds
& Stuart Townend

With a steady rhythm

125

58   In the beauty of holiness

Robin Mark

1. In the beau-ty of ho-li-ness   we see you,— Son of
I could bring,   was there e-ver a

right-eous-ness,   so we bring all— that we pos-sess—
song to sing   that could e-ver— ex-press, my King,—

to lay— at your feet;   in the place— where your
the work— that you've done?   Could I e-ver con-

glo-ry shines.   Je-sus, lo-ver of all man-kind,
ceive of this,   all the depths and the heights and breadth

you have drawn us— with love di - vine— to make— us com -
of the rich - es— I now pos - sess— be - cause— of your

plete. So I'll pause at your gates once more, as my heart and my
love.

Chorus

spi - rit soar, and I wish I— could love you more, my God and my

(Fine)

King.

1. 2. Is there tri - bute— that

D.C.

2. So I'll pause at your

D.S.

59   I praise you for your faithfulness

Robin Mark

love for me en-dures. (Men) When I think, (Women) when I think, on all these things, (All) on all these things, O I love you more and more, I praise you for your faith-ful-ness O Lord.

59a   Declaration of Faith

To whom shall we go?
You have the words of eternal life,
and we have believed and have come to know
that You are the Holy One of God.
Praise to You, Lord Jesus Christ,
King of endless glory.

Words from John 6 arranged by John Polce
(used in Morning Office from Celtic Daily Prayer © Northumbria Community Trust Ltd)

60 I've filled my days with details
(Be still)

Reflective

David Gate

1. I've filled my days with de-tails ___ and all the choi-ces of ___ the earth, ___ car-ried the yoke of wor-ry, ___ and all the bur-dens that ___ it brings. ___ And through the midst of all ___ the rush-ing, ___ you ___ whis-per to ___ our hearts, ___ and with ___ your sweet voice ___ you say to us:

2. So give me peace and wis-dom ___ to know how to fill ___ my time, ___ where I can learn to keep you ___ at the cen-tre of ___ my life. So through the midst of all ___ the rush-ing ___ there is time to spend ___ with you, ___ and my ___ foun-da-tion ___ will dai-ly be:

61

I will bow down
(Worthy of all)

Keith Deal

♩ = 74

1. I will bow down,   lay my pride down,   I will wor-ship you.___
2. I will love you,   none a-bove you,   you make all things new.___

You're my Ma-ker,   my Cre-a-tor,   there is none like you.___
You're my Heal-er,   my Re-deem-er,   there is none like you.___

All through my life you have___ been   faith-ful and true,___
All through my life you will___ be   faith-ful and true,___

Chorus

I'm bow-ing down to wor-ship   you. You are wor-thy of all,___
I'm bow-ing down to wor-ship   you.

you are wor-thy of all,___ and all my life___ I'll live for you,___
do the things___ you want me to:___ I will wor-ship you.___

61a   Make known his faithfulness

Psalm 89: 1–2

I will sing of the Lord's great love for ever;
 with my mouth I will make your faithfulness
  known through all generations.
I will declare that your love stands firm for ever,
 that you have established your faithfulness
  in heaven itself.

62 I will come, come, come
(All)

Tim Sherrington

Capo 1 (D)
Rhythmically, with anticipation

63 I will love you Lord forever
(Taste and see)

From Psalm 34
Tré & Tori Sheppard

Driving ♩ = 108

1. I will love you, Lord, for e - ver, my lips will al - ways sing
(2.) looked for you and, oh, you found me, de - li - vered me from all

your name. From deep in - side I feel it ris - ing, come
my fears. With hearts wide o - pen, our fa - ces shin - ing, our

glo - ri - fy the Lord with me, come glo - ri - fy the Lord
shame is gone as you draw near, our shame is gone as you

with me. I taste and see that you are good, I
draw near.

hide my-self___ with-in___ your___ love.___ In your___ pre - sence I___

___ lack___ no - thing, you're all I want___ and you___ are here___ with___

___ me.___

(Fine)

D.C.

2. I

64 Jesus, be the centre

Moderately

Michael Frye

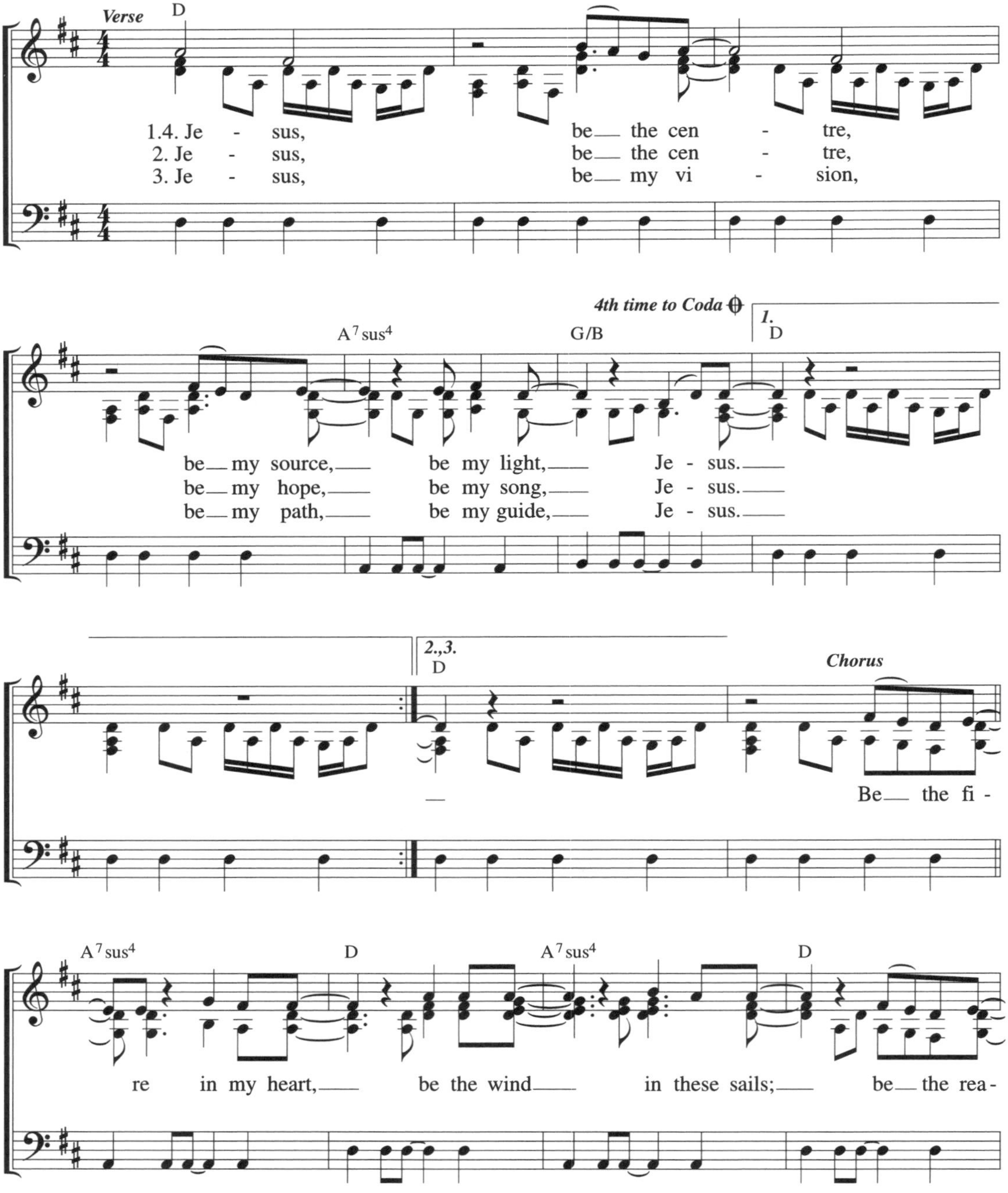

Verse
D
1.4. Je - sus, be the cen - tre,
2. Je - sus, be the cen - tre,
3. Je - sus, be my vi - sion,
A7sus4
4th time to Coda
G/B
1.
D
be my source, be my light, Je - sus.
be my hope, be my song, Je - sus.
be my path, be my guide, Je - sus.
2.,3.
D
Chorus
Be the fi -
A7sus4
D
A7sus4
D
re in my heart, be the wind in these sails; be the rea -

son that I live,_____ Je - sus,_____ Je - sus._____

64a   An opening prayer

God of our days and years,
we set this time apart for you.
Form us in the likeness of Christ
so that our lives may glorify you.
Amen.

65 Jesus Christ is waiting

NOËL NOUVELET

Words: John L. Bell
Music: French Trad.
Arr. David Ball

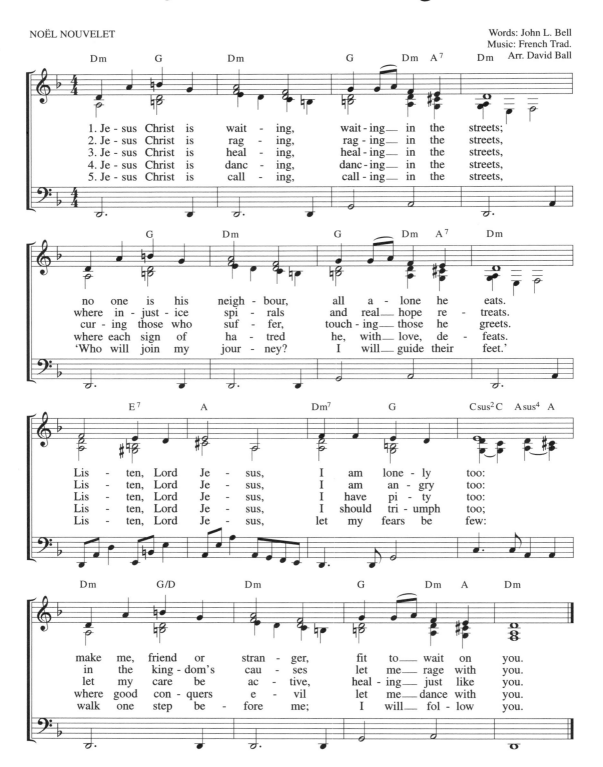

1. Je - sus Christ is wait - ing, wait - ing in the streets;
2. Je - sus Christ is rag - ing, rag - ing in the streets,
3. Je - sus Christ is heal - ing, heal - ing in the streets,
4. Je - sus Christ is danc - ing, danc - ing in the streets,
5. Je - sus Christ is call - ing, call - ing in the streets,

no one is his neigh - bour, all a - lone he eats.
where in - just - ice spi - rals and real hope re - treats.
cur - ing those who suf - fer, touch - ing those he greets.
where each sign of ha - tred he, with love, de - feats.
'Who will join my jour - ney? I will guide their feet.'

Lis - ten, Lord Je - sus, I am lone - ly too:
Lis - ten, Lord Je - sus, I am an - gry too:
Lis - ten, Lord Je - sus, I have pi - ty too:
Lis - ten, Lord Je - sus, I should tri - umph too;
Lis - ten, Lord Je - sus, let my fears be few:

make me, friend or stran - ger, fit to wait on you.
in the king - dom's cau - ses let me rage with you.
let my care be ac - tive, heal - ing just like you.
where good con - quers e - vil let me dance with you.
walk one step be - fore me; I will fol - low you.

Bridges to D

66

Jesus Christ
(All my love)

Noel Richards

Steadily

1. Je - sus Christ, you came in - to this world to re -
   (2.) safe up - on the o - cean of your mer -
   (3.) stand up - on your pro - mise of e - ter -

- scue me. On the cross my sin was
- cy. I am loved with all the
- nal grace. I be - lieve that I will

laid on you, what a - go - ny. There your
pas - sion of e - ter - ni - ty. It is
one day see you face to face. I will

pre - cious life blood flowed so free, e - v'ry drop that fell still clean -
deep - er than the deep - est sea, like a ti - dal wave, it car -
wor - ship you for - e - ver-more in ways I ne - ver have -

66a Made alive in Christ

Ephesians 2: 4–5

But because of his great love for us, God, who is rich in mercy,
made us alive with Christ even when we were dead in transgressions –
it is by grace you have been saved. And God raised us up with Christ
and seated us with him in the heavenly realms in Christ Jesus...

67 Jesus is Lord!

Daniel Chua

1. Je-sus is Lord! Be-hold the King of kings, ex-al-ted high, the name a-bove all names. I sing his praise, the Lamb up-on the throne, who reigns in glo-ry, pow'r and ma-je-sty.

2. This is my claim: 'Je-sus is Lord, Je-sus is
God. Be-hold his hands and side, the wounds of love that healed my bro-ken-ness. What God is this? What kind of sa-cri-fice would give so much to gain a love-less soul?

3. For me to live is Christ, to die is gain, for Christ has died that I might gain his life. He is my all, my joy, my righ-teous-ness, my hope of glo-ry when he comes to reign.

4. Yes, sud-den-ly my God shall come a-gain, and e-v'ry knee shall bow be-fore his name. And he shall reign for-e-ver on the throne, and in his glo-ry there shall I pro-

Lord,   Je - sus is Lord,   Je - sus is Lord!'

67a   The earth is the Lord's

Psalm 24

The earth is the Lord's and everything in it,
the world, and all who live in it;
for he founded it upon the seas
and established it upon the waters.

Who may ascend the hill of the Lord?
Who may stand in his holy place?
He who has clean hands and a pure heart,
who does not lift up his soul to an idol or swear by what is
false.

He will receive blessing from the Lord
and vindication from God his Saviour.
Such is the generation of those who seek him,
who seek your face, O God of Jacob.

Lift up your heads, O you gates;
be lifted up, you ancient doors,
that the King of glory may come in.

Who is this King of glory?
The Lord strong and mighty,
the Lord mighty in battle.

Lift up your heads, O you gates;
lift them up, you ancient doors,
that the King of glory may come in.
Who is he, this King of glory?
The Lord Almighty –
he is the King of glory.

Joy Townhill

Jesus loves the church
(Can you hear him singing?)

Capo 1 (D)
With strength

Michael Sandeman

1. Je-sus loves the church,— he gave him-self— for his bride.
2. Je-sus loves the church,— his pas-sion through— the a-ges.

He knows what we will be,— a con-quer-ing ar-
Hell will not pre-vail,— he builds us to-ge-

my, an un-blem-ished peo - ple. We're ac-cep-ted,— we're for-
ther, a li - ving tem - ple. We're ac-cep-ted,— we're for-

giv-en,— we're u-ni-ted— with him; not re-jec-ted,— not for-
giv-en,— we're u-ni-ted— with him; not re-jec-ted,— not for-

68a   The bride of Christ

John 3: 29–30

The bride belongs to the bridegroom. The friend who attends the
bridegroom waits and listens for him, and is full of joy when he hears
the bridegroom's voice. That joy is mine, and it is now complete.
He must become greater; I must become less.

69 Jesus, name above all names
(The Jesus song)

Steadily

Owen Hurter

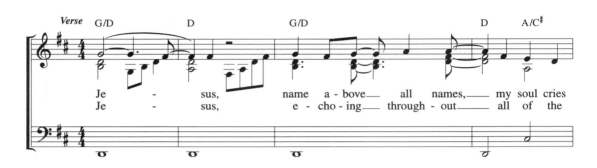

Verse

Je - sus, name a - bove all names, my soul cries
Je - sus, e - cho - ing through - out all of the

Je - sus, it's the sweet - est song.
hea - vens, an - ge - lic hosts pro - claim.

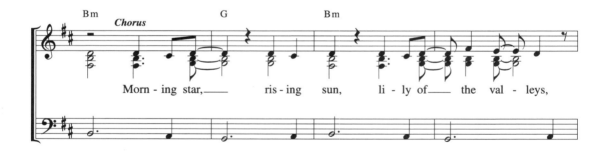

Chorus

Morn - ing star, ris - ing sun, li - ly of the val - leys,

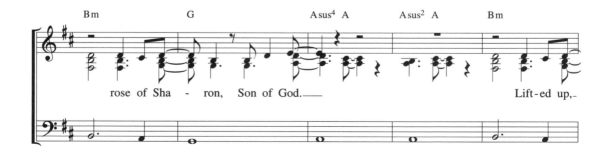

rose of Sha - ron, Son of God. Lift - ed up,

glo-ri-fied,____ praised through all____ the a - ges: the first and last,_

be - gin - ning and_____ end.____

69a Prayer of Preparation

Almighty God,
to whom all hearts are open,
all desires known,
and from whom no secrets are hidden:
cleanse the thoughts of our hearts
by the inspiration of your Holy Spirit,
that we may perfectly love you,
and worthily magnify your holy name;
through Christ our Lord.
Amen.

Jesus, Redeemer
(Redeemer)

Tim Hughes

Jesus you alone

Capo 4(G)
Driving

Tim Hughes

1. Je-sus, you a-lone must be my first love, my first love. The se-cret place and high-est praise shall be yours, shall be yours. To your throne I'll bring de-vo-tion, may it be the sweet-est sound: Lord, this heart is

2. Day and night I lift my eyes to seek you, to seek you. Hun-gry for a glimpse of you in glo-ry, in glo-ry.

reach - ing for you now.

Chorus

So I'll set my sights ___ up - on ___ you,
You a - lone will be ___ my pas - sion,

set my life up - on ___
Je - sus, you will be ___

— your praise; ___ ne - ver look - ing to ___ a - no - ther way. ___
— my song: ___ you will find me long -

ing af - ter you. ___

D.C. (Last time D.S.) | *To end*

72

Jina la Yesu libarikiwe

4 part harmony

Trad. Kenyan
Arr. Christopher Norton

Ji - na la Ye - su li - ba - ri - ki - we, Ji - na la Ye - su li - ba - ri -
Bless that won - der - ful name of Je - sus, bless that won - der - ful name of

ki - we, Ji - na la Ye - su li - ba - ri - ki - we, Ji - na la ngu - vu zo - te.
Je - sus, bless that won - der - ful name of Je - sus, no o - ther name I know.

Rhythm for English words

Bless that won - der - ful name of Je - sus.

72a   A Declaration of Praise

Leader: Praise the Lord! King of kings.
All: **We come before him with singing.**
Leader: Praise the Lord! King of creation.
All: **We come before him in wonder.**
Leader: Praise the Lord! King of love.
All: **We come before him with thanks.**
Leader: Praise the Lord! King Jesus
All: **We come before him as an offering.**

73 Lead us heavenly Father

4 part harmony

Words: James Edmeston
Music: Geraldine Latty

1. Lead us, hea-v'nly Fa-ther, lead us through this world's tem-pes-tuous
2. Sa-viour, by your grace re-store us all our weak-nes-ses are
3. Spi-rit of our God, de-scend-ing, fill our hearts with ho-ly

sea; guard us, guide us, keep us, feed us - you our on-ly help and
plain; you have lived on earth be-fore us, you have felt our grief and
peace; love with e-v'ry pas-sion blend-ing, plea-sure that can ne-ver

plea; here pos-sess-ing ev-'ry bless-ing if our God our Fa-ther be.
pain: temp-ted, taun-ted, yet un-daun-ted, from the depths you rose a-gain.
cease: thus pro-vi-ded, par-doned, gui-ded, e-ver shall our joys in-crease.

74

Lamp unto my feet
(It is you)

Steadily

Darlene Zschech

1. Lamp unto to my feet, light unto to my path, it is
trea-sure that I hold, more than fi-nest gold, it is

you, Je-sus, it is you. 2. This
you,

Je-sus, it is you. With all my heart,

with all my soul, I live to wor-ship you and praise

for-e-ver-more, praise for e-ver-more.

Lord, e-v'ry day___ I need___ you more,___ on wings___ of hea-

ven I___ will soar___ with you.___

Last time to Coda

Verse

3. You take___ my bro-ken-ness,___ call___ me

to your-self,___ there you___ stand,___ heal-ing in___ your hands.___

D.S. al Coda Coda

Rit . . .

157

75

Let the exile come
(Come heal this land)

Robin Mark

Let the ex - ile come,____ let the stran - ger come, let the
ta - ble waits____ in your Fa - ther's house, there the

wea - ry come find rest; all you home - less sons, all you
meek can come and eat; there's a place of rest at your

wi - dowed ones, all you poor and dis - pos - sessed. For a
Fa - ther's breast, where his mer - cy

is com - plete.

1. Does a cry____ ring out
2. Do the tears____ of One
3. So may this land____ we love

(continued over...)

selves - be - fore you, we hum - ble — our - selves.

Chorus

Come heal this land, come heal this land,

come heal this land, come heal this land.

land.

160

76 Let your glory fill this temple

Capo 1(G)

DIM OND IESU

Words: Andy Smith & Johnny Markin
Music: Robert Lowry (1826-99)

1. Let your glo-ry fill this tem-ple,— may you find a wel-come here. May this ga-th'ring of your peo-ple— find their hope and com-fort near. Let the glo-ry of your pre-sence— spur us on to work for you; we are wil-ling to be chan-nels— for your pow-er to flow through.

2. May the wea-ry and the woun-ded— find their strength to rise a-gain as the heal-er moves a-mongst us,— hear him call each one by name. Grace un-end-ing here is flow-ing— strength will come to all who wait. Je-sus, heal the bro-ken heart-ed,— cause to soar the weak and faint.

3. May the church-es stand to-ge-ther— as we rise to sing as one; for the heal-ing of the na-tions,— e-v'ry land un-der the Son. All God's peo-ple join the cho-rus,— sing it out near and a-broad: till all na-tions bow in wor-ship,— all con-fess Je-sus is Lord.

77

Light of the world
(Here I am to worship)

Gradually building

Tim Hughes

1. Light of the world, you stepped down into darkness, opened my eyes, let me see. Beauty that made this heart adore you, hope of a life spent with you.

2. King of all days, oh so highly exalted, glorious in heaven above, humbly you came to the earth you created, all for love's sake became poor.

Chorus

So here I am to worship, here I am to bow down, here I am to say that you're my God: you're altogether lovely, altogether

This song is recorded on the Spring Harvest 2001 Praise Mix Album

78

Lord I come to you
(How can I do anything but praise you)

Capo 3(D)
With intensity

Colse Leung

Lord, I come___ to you,___ (I'm) bro-ken___ and lost,___
Here I am___ a-gain,___ (I'm) long-ing___ for more,___

Je-sus, be___ the high-est part.___
wait-ing for___ your pre-sence here,___

your pre-sence___ here.___ And

how can I do___ a - ny-thing but praise___ you,
Lord, you a-maze___ me with___ your fa - vour,

how can I not— wor - ship you,—
Lord, you a-stound— me— with your love,

and how can I live— my life—

— with-out— you, God?—

2nd time D.C. | *To end*
F(D)

78a   Praise the Lord!

Psalm 145: 10–13

All you have made will praise you, O Lord;
     your saints will extol you.
They will tell of the glory of your kingdom
     and speak of your might,
so that all men may know of your mighty acts
     and the glorious splendour of your kingdom.
Your kingdom is an everlasting kingdom,
     and your dominion endures through all generations.

79

Lord let the nations see
(You alone are God)

Keith Deal

fan the flames,___ let the pas - sion burn___ a - gain.___ Take the sword,_

break the chains,___ Lord we're call - ing out.___ You a - lone___ are___ God,_

you a - lone___ are___ King:___ Sa - viour of___ the world,___

Lord of e - v'ry thing.___ Come with heal - ing pow'r,___

set the cap - tives free,___ let the de - sert flow'r,___

(continued over...)

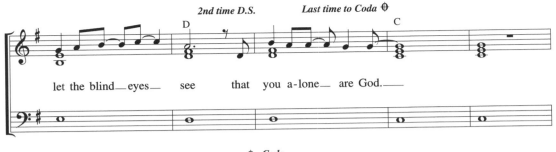

let the blind eyes see that you a-lone are God.

You a-lone are God.

79a   In Declaration of a Dream

I cannot speak,
unless You loose my tongue;
I only stammer,
and I speak uncertainly;
but if You touch my mouth,
My Lord,
then I will sing the story
of Your wonders!

So many who have heard
forget to tell the story.

Here am I, my Jesus:
teach me.

From the Caedmon liturgy ('In Declaration of a Dream')
Celtic Daily Prayer, © Northumbria Community Trust Ltd

80 Lord, take this song
(Haven song)

Andy Raine
& Andy Robertson

1. Lord, take this song and fill it with your pre-sence, let it bring a word of hope to wea-ry, care-ful hearts. Take this song and fill it Lord, fill it with your-self.

2. Lord, take my life and fill it with your prai-ses, let me speak a word of peace that Je-sus brings in me. Take this life and fill it, Lord, fill it with your-self.

3. Lord, take this place and fill it with your bles-sing, let it be a ha-ven where the poor in spi-rit sing. Take this place and fill it, Lord, fill it with your praise.

81 Lord of the church

LONDONDERRY AIR

Lyrically

Words: Timothy Dudley-Smith
Music: Irish traditional melody
Arr. David Ball

1. Lord of the church, we pray for our re - new - ing:
church, we seek a Fat - her's bles - sing,
church, we long for our u - nit - ing,

Christ o - ver all, our un - di - vi - ded aim. Fire of the
a true re - pen - tance and a faith re - stored, a swift o -
true to one cal - ling, by one vi - sion stirred; one cross pro -

Spi - rit, burn for our en - du - ing, wind of the Spi - rit,
be - dience and a new pos - ses - sing, filled with the Ho - ly
claim - ing and one creed re - cit - ing, one in the truth of

fan the liv - ing flame! We turn to Christ a - mid our fear and
Spi - rit of the Lord! We turn to Christ from all our rest - less
Je - sus and his word! So lead us on; till toil and trou - ble

Musical score with lyrics:

Verse lines under the staves:

fail - ing,____ the will that lacks the cou-rage to be free,____
striv - ing,____ un - num - bered voi - ces with a sin - gle pray'r=____
end - ed,____ one church tr - i - umph - ant one new song shall sing,____

_ the wea - ry la - bours, all but un - a - vail - ing,____ to bring us
_ the liv - ing wa - ter for our soul's re - viv - ing,____ in Christ to
_ to praise his glo - ry, ri - sen and as - cen - ded,____ Christ o - ver

near - er what a church____ should be. 2. Lord of the
live, and love and serve____ and care. 3. Lord of the
all, the e - ver - last - ing King!

81a   Love

1 Corinthians 13: 4–7

Love is patient, love is kind.
It does not envy, it does not boast, it is not proud.
It is not rude, it is not self-seeking, it is not easily angered,
it keeps no record of wrongs.
Love does not delight in evil but rejoices with the truth.
It always protects, always trusts, always hopes, always perseveres.

82

Lord we lift you high

♩ = 86

Judy Bailey

83 Lord, you've been good to me

Graham Kendrick

1. Lord, you've been good to me all my life, all my life; your loving kindness never fails. I will remember all you have done, bring from my heart thanksgiving songs.

2. So may each breath I take be for you, Lord, only you, giving you back the life I owe. Love so amazing, mercy so free. Lord, you've been good, so good to me.

New ev-'ry morn - ing is your love,
filled with com-pas - sion from a-bove.
Grace and for-give - ness full and free,
Lord, you've been good to me.

84

Love is bigger than oceans
(Not forgotten)

Martin Smith

1. { Love is big-ger—than o - ceans,—
   Grace is big-ger—than his - t'ry,—
2. { Faith is big-ger—than glo - ry,—
   Hope is high - er—than rain - bows,—

love is gi - ven— to me.
grace is gi - ven— for free.
faith is stron - ger— than pain.
hope is all that— we've got.

we'll keep the flame a - blaze.— He— (You)

—— will not—————— be for - got - ten,— be for-

got - ten.

got - ten.

D.C. (v.2)

got - ten.

D.S. Chorus 2 ⊕ *Coda*

got - ten,_____

— be for - got - ten,_____ be - for - got - ten,_____

— be for - got - ten_____

177

Love like a jewel
(I will seek after you)

Sue Rinaldi,
& Steve Bassett

♩ = 80

This song is recorded on the Spring Harvest 2002 New Songs Album

sake e - v'ry thing— that is dis - trac - ting me— from this search - ing,— and run to the place— where my heart— on - ly hears— the beat— of your love— for this world.—

86 May the words of my mouth

Tim Hughes
& Rob Hill

Moving with the Father
(Joy)

Ken Riley

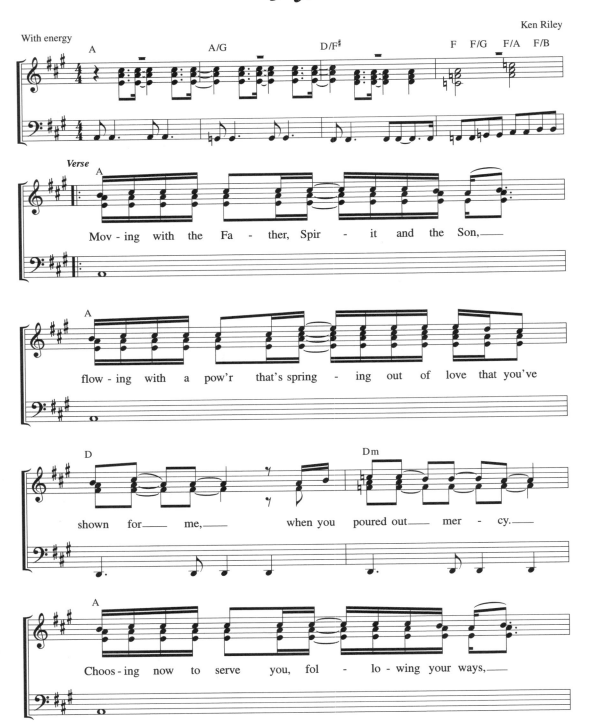

This song is recorded on the *Spring Harvest 2002 Praise Mix Album*

(continued over...)

joy. Joy,＿ Lord, I dance with＿ joy,＿

Jump-ing in＿ the pre-sence of my＿ God.＿

To verse

_ God.＿

To bridge

Your mer-cy's new＿ each day,＿ and shin-ing like＿ the sun:＿

you'll be my song＿ of praise＿ un - til my race＿ is run,＿

185

88

My hope is built on nothing less
(On Christ the solid Rock)

Words: Edward Mote (1797 - 1874)
Music: William B. Bradbury (1816 - 1868)
arr. Robert Critchley

Chorus

dare not trust the sweet - est frame, but whol - ly lean on Je - sus'
all a - round my soul gives way, he then is all my hope and
in his right - eous - ness a - lone, fault - less to stand be - fore the

name. On Christ the so - lid rock I stand, all o - ther ground is
stay.
throne.

sink - ing sand, all o - ther ground is sink - ing sand. 2. When

sand. 3. When sand. On sand.

187

89 My hope rests firm on Jesus Christ

Liltingly

Keith Getty
& Richard Creighton

1. My hope rests firm on Je-sus Christ, he is my on-ly
(2.) hope su-stains me as I strive and strain to-wards the
(3.) hope pro-vides me with a spur to help me run this
(4.) hope is to be with my Lord, to know as I am

plea. Though all the world should point and scorn; his
goal; though still I stum-ble in-to sin his
race. I know my tears will turn to joy the
known; to serve him glad-ly all my days in

ran-som leaves me free, his ran-som leaves me
death pays for it all, his death pays for it
day I see his face, the day I see his
praise be-fore his throne, in praise be-fore his

free.
all.
face.
throne.

Last time

2. My
3. My
4. My

Multi-dimensional Worship

CREATEgenerateinventinnovateformulateinitiatelaunchactivateimagine

When we gather at events such as Spring Harvest or those organised in your local church venues or even in your own living room, we create together a worship environment. Within that worship environment we offer up visible, audible and tangible expressions of thankfulness, intimacy, devotion, praise.....authentic and diverse expressions that flow from lives that are journeying with the Saviour, on a search to explore the heart of the heart of God.

Corporate worship environments have the capacity to be incredibly multi-dimensional. Our outward expressions of worship can be musical, vocal, artistic or visual; in the form of dance and movement, video and images, spontaneous music or organised songs. There can also be inward expressions of worship, in the form of silence, prayer and meditation. We often need to be reminded that God is a creative God with infinite imagination and resources, and as people made in the image of God, we inherit this creative potential.

An added feature to this years songbook is the inclusion of a number of songs that can be used effectively as a solo piece by an artist or a band or music group (see 'Suitable for solo or presentation' in the Thematic Index for more details). These songs can really enhance the worship environment and we need to learn to listen to these with the same openness and sensitivity that we display when we are singing a more familiar tune all together in the more traditional way. Perhaps over recent years we have dismissed the art of 'listening' as a valid form of participative worship and sadly we have relegated it to a passive activity. However, listening to a well selected and appropriate song can inspire and provoke, and minister directly to hearts and minds. Melvyn Bragg eloquently remarks that art, which includes music and song, 'crystallises feelings and emotions, penetrates the imagination, belongs to the spiritual and promises glimpses of another world'!

We need to face a fresh challenge to un-box 'worship' and go in search of hidden treasure. As we explore multi-dimensional expressions of worship with dance, music, performed song, poetry, silence, ritual, symbolism, video, images, painting, installation art, and as we encourage one another to move out of our comfort zones, we will discover a greater level of sensitivity and freedom to the Holy Spirit and to one another.

Sue Rinaldi

90 My soul praises the Lord
(Mary's song)

Andy Flannagan

Moderately

91 Name above all names

Capo 3(D)

Neil Bennetts

Worshipfully

1. Name a- bove all names, the Sa - viour for sin -
2. Gi - ver of mer - cy, the foun - tain of life
3. High King e - ter - nal, the one true and faith -

- ners slain. You suf - fered for my sake,
- for me. My spi - rit is lift - ed,
ful God. The beau - ti - ful Sa - viour,

to bring me back home a - gain. When I was lost, you
to soar on the ea - gles' wings. What love is this that
still reign-ing in pow'r and love. With all my heart I'll

poured your life out for me. Name a-bove all names,
fills my heart with trea - sure? Name a-bove all names,
wor - ship you for - e - ver: name a-bove all names,

Je-sus, I love___ you.
Je-sus, I love___ you.
Je-sus, I love___ you.

Last time
F(D)

91a   A prayer for Resurrection Power

Almighty God,
who raised Jesus from the dead
and exalted him to your right hand on high:
may we know your resurrection power in our daily lives
and look with hope to that day
when we shall see you face to face
and share in your glory,
Father, Son and Holy Spirit:
one God, now and forever.
Amen.

92 None other

Geraldine Latty

Steadily

None o - ther is more wor - thy, none o - ther is more de-serv- ing of—our praise.— None o - ther is so ho - ly, sov-'reign God— we come— to you, we will give— the glo - ry due your name.—

None oth -

93

O Lord, hear
(Breathe on us again)

94

O hallelujah!
(Lift him high)

Mark Bradford

This song is recorded on the Spring Harvest 2002 Praise Mix Album

95

O my God
(Your loving kindness)

Psalm 63: 1-7

Russ Hughes

Capo 3 (D)

1. O my God, how I long for you; my heart is filled
2. O my God, how I long for you; my heart it yearns

with just one breath from you. O my God,
for just one glimpse of you. O my God,

my soul is wait - ing to be sa - tis - fied
I am list' - ning and wait - ing, Lord,

with one more drink from you. For I have seen you in the sanc-
to hear your song of love.

96 O sacred King

Matt Redman

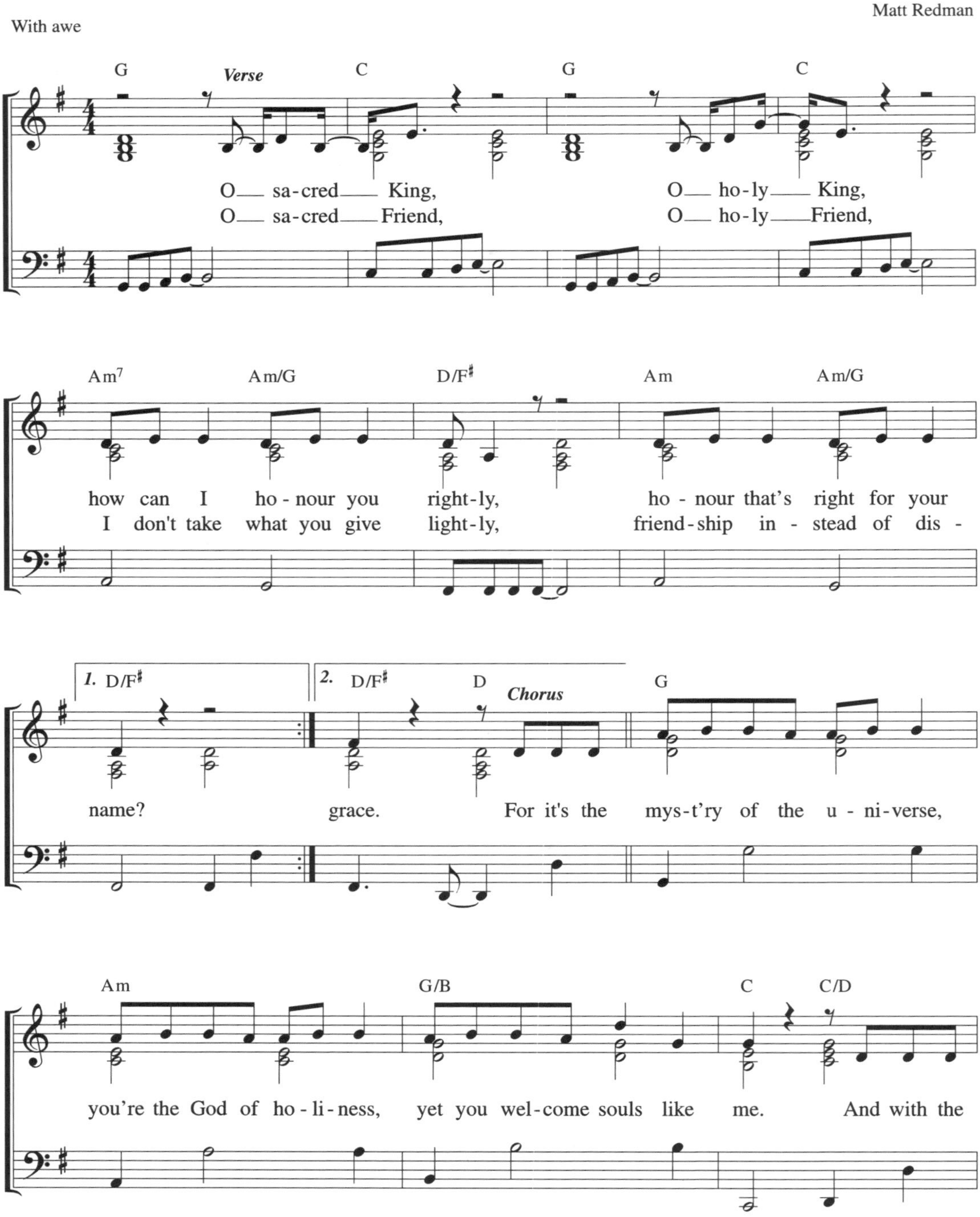

With awe
G
Verse
C
G
C
O sa-cred King, O ho-ly King,
O sa-cred Friend, O ho-ly Friend,
Am7
Am/G
D/F#
Am
Am/G
how can I ho-nour you right-ly, ho-nour that's right for your
I don't take what you give light-ly, friend-ship in-stead of dis-
1. D/F#
2. D/F#
D
Chorus
G
name? grace. For it's the mys-t'ry of the u-ni-verse,
Am
G/B
C
C/D
you're the God of ho-li-ness, yet you wel-come souls like me. And with the

bles-sing of your Fa-ther's heart, you dis-ci-pline the ones you love, there's

kind-ness in your ma-jes-ty.____ Je-sus, those who re-cog-nise your

pow'r, know just how won-der-ful you are, that you draw near.

96a   Offertory Prayer

Heavenly Father,
let these gifts go where we cannot go,
and help those whom we cannot reach;
through them
let the unlearned be taught,
the hungry fed,
the sick healed
and the lost found;
for Jesus' sake.
Amen.

97 O the love of God is boundless

Words D.R. Edwards
Revised and adapted by Graham Kendrick
Music: Graham Kendrick
arr. Richard Lewis

1. O, the love of God is bound-less, per-fect, cause-less,___ full___ and___ free! Doubts have va-nished, fears are ground-less, now I know___ that___ love___ to___ me.

2. O, the cross of Christ is won-drous! There I learn___ God's heart___ to___ me; 'midst the si-lent, deep'-ning dark-ness 'God is light' I___ al-so___ see.

3. O, the sight of heav'n is glo-rious! Man in right-eous-ness___ is___ there. Once the vic-tim, now vic-to-ri-ous, Je-sus lives___ in___ glo-ry___ fair!

4. O, what rest of soul in see-ing Je-sus on___ his___ Fa-ther's___ throne! Yes, what peace for e-ver-flow-ing from God's rest___ in___ his___ own___ Son!

Love, the source— of all my bless - ing, love that set— it -
Ho - ly claims— of jus - tice find - ing full ex - pres - sion—
Him, who met— the claims of glo - ry and the need— of—
Gaz - ing up - ward in - to hea - ven, read - ing glo - ry—

self on me. Love, that gave— the sin - less vic - tim, love, told out— at—
in that scene; light and love— a - like are tel - ling what his woe— and—
ru - ined man on the cross, O won - drous sto - ry! God has set— at—
in his face, know - ing that— 'tis he, once gi - ven on the cross— to—

Cal - va - ry.
suff' - ring means.
his right hand.
take my place.

97a   The forgiveness of God

Romans 4: 7–8

Blessed are they whose transgressions are forgiven,
    whose sins are covered.
Blessed is the man
    whose sin the Lord will never count against him.

98 Oh the love of my Lord is the essence

Estelle White

99

One Lord, one faith
(Increase in me)

Steve & Velveta Thompson
& Andy Mitchell

Steadily

1. One Lord, one faith, we stand to-ge-ther.
One God and Fa-ther of us all.
In u-ni-ty and by God's Spi-rit,
we walk as one to reach our goal.

2. To reach the lost is our com-mis-sion,
to stretch our hands to those in need:
re-flect God's heart, ful-fil his call-ing
and then his king-dom will in-crease.

(continued over...)

99a Watch and Pray

From Matthew 26: 41; 20: 28 & Luke 23: 34

Watch and pray, that you may not come into the time of trial.
Lord, help us to say with Jesus,
'Your will, not mine, be done.'

The spirit is willing, but the flesh is weak.
Lord, help us to say with Jesus,
'I am here to serve, not to be served.'

Watch and pray, that you may not come into the time of trial.
Lord help us to say with Jesus,
'Father, forgive them.'

The spirit is willing but the flesh is weak.
Lord, help us to say with Jesus,
'Your will, not mine, be done.'

Copyright © Mark Earey

100 One sacrifice and I am free

James Gregory

Brightly

Verse

E

One sa-cri-fice____ and I____ am free,____ the cross of Christ____

Je-sus, in death____ you set____ me free,____ tak-ing the pun-

E/D♯

A sus²

_ my vic-to-ry,____ and on this grace____ I do____ be-lieve,-

ish-ment for me,____ it is your blood____ that co-vers me,-

E

E/D♯

_ yes, I be-lieve.____

_ yes, I be-lieve.-

1. **A sus²**

2. **A sus²**

_ And be-cause-

A **G♯m⁷** **A** **F♯m¹¹**

of what this love____ has done___ my heart____ is filled with praise.____

This song is recorded on the *Spring Harvest 2002 Praise Mix Album*

And so I lift___ my voice___ to you,___
I know the Sa - viour lives___ to day,___

pour-ing out all___ this love___ on you,___ what can I give___
hea - ven and earth___ may pass___ a - way,___ but I___ know___

_ for all___ you've done___ for me?___   - ver fail,___
_ your love___ will ne -

Last time to Coda
no, no.___

And e - v'ry day___ I live___ I vow___ to fol - low you.___

(continued over...)

100a   A Listening Prayer

Based on Revelation 3: 13

Jesus, you said 'He who has an ear,
let him hear what the Spirit says to the churches.'

**Jesus, I want to hear.
Amen.**

Joy Townhill

Bridges to F

211

101

Only you
(Nothing compares to you)

Medium pace

James Taylor

1. On - ly you___ can re - place___ rags for rich -
(2.)___ de - mons flee,___ moun - tains trem -
(3.)___ such a cost,___ so much more -
(4.)___ to the cross___ where the tears___

es pure___ as gold,___ and your mer - cy saved___ my soul,
ble in your sight,___ but you love me like a friend,
_ than can be won: God, you gave___ your on - ly Son,
_ of hea - ven fall, you have heard the sin - ner's call:

there's none like you.
there's none like you.___
there's none like you.___
there's none like you._

2. At your name___

4. So we'll bow___

No - thing com - pares___ to you,___

This song is recorded on the Spring Harvest 2001 Praise Mix Album

you're the one we love   send

down your ho - ly fire   o - ver all the earth.

No

3. You have paid

213

102 Open the eyes of my heart

Paul Baloche

Ho - ly, ho - ly, ho - ly,— ho - ly, ho - ly, ho - ly,—

ho - ly, ho - ly, ho - ly,— I want to see— you.—

to fade

102a   Praising God as we go

The Lord God Almighty is our Father:
he loves us and tenderly cares for us.

The Lord Jesus Christ is our Saviour:
he has redeemed us and will defend us to the end.

The Lord, the Holy Spirit, is among us:
he will lead us in God's holy way.

**To God Almighty, Father, Son and Holy Spirit,
be praise and glory today and forever. Amen.**

103   Our God is a great big God

With a 'Gospel' feel

Jo & Nigel Hemming

Chorus

Our God is a great big God, our God is a great big God,

Last time to Coda

our God is a great big God and he holds us in his hands.

Verse

He's high-er than a sky-scrap-er and he's

deep-er than a sub-ma-rine. He's wi-der than the u-ni-verse and be-

yond my wild-est dreams.____ And he's known____ me and____ he's loved____ me since be-fore the world____ be-gan.____ How won-der-ful____ to be a part____ of God's a-maz-ing plan.____

great big God and he holds us in his hands.____ And he

217

104

Over all the earth
(Lord, reign in me)

Brenton Brown

♩ = 106

1. Ov-er all the earth, you reign on high, ev-ery moun-tain stream,
2. Ov-er e-v'ry thought, ov-er e-v'ry word, may my life re-flect

ev-ery sun-set sky. But my one re-quest,
the beau-ty of my Lord; 'cause you mean more to me

Lord, my on-ly aim is that you'd reign in me a-gain.
than a-ny earth-ly thing. So won't you reign in me a-gain.

Chorus

Lord, reign in me, reign in your power; ov-er all my dreams,

105 Over the mountains and the sea
(I could sing of your love forever)

Capo 3(D)

Martin Smith

Steadily

Ov-er the moun-tains and— the sea your riv-er runs— with love— for me,

and I will o-pen up my heart,— and let the Heal-er set— me free.

I'm hap-py to— be in— the truth, and I will dai-ly lift— my hands,

for I will— al-ways sing of when your love came down, yeah.—

I could sing of your love— for-ev-er, I could sing of your love—

106 Perfect beauty (Temple song)
(You are the One)

Andy Flannagan

With energy

1. Per - fect beau - ty____ con - tained in____ a____ man,____
2. Help____ me build you____ this tem - ple of____ praise,____

King____ of hea - ven____ who walked in____ the____ sand.____
firm____ foun - da - tions____ so set in your____ ways.____

Can____ a hu - man____ house the di - vine?____
Not____ a - shamed to____ now wel - come____ you in;

Can____ your Spi - rit flow in - to mine? Build me____ with____ your
since____ your blood has____ de - le - ted____ my sin. As my____ spi - rit

This song is recorded on the Spring Harvest 2002 Praise Mix Album

pre - cious stone, then move in - to your right - ful home.
aches and groans, move right in to take your throne.

Chorus

You are the One who has come to this temple. Come take con - trol of my soul and my mind. Teach me to fall on my face in your pre - sence.

(continued over...)

Working with the PA Engineer in worship

And the fellowship all met together in one place and asked, 'Who will be most important in the kingdom of God – a keyboard operator or a keyboard player?

I'm sure that the hypothetical question posed above has never actually been voiced but it does serve to highlight topical issues and reminds us that we should remember to encourage each other, whatever our gifting, and none more than the back room technicians. They often only get noticed when they get it wrong.

It seems the disciples asked similar questions of Jesus on numerous occasions and clearly argued amongst themselves about this subject. In 1 Corinthians when Paul was speaking about the gifts of the Spirit he said quite clearly that we are all part of one serving body and none is more important than the other. I believe that when God looks down and sees the collective talents which are bought together when we worship he smiles with some satisfaction.

Not only for example, are musicians and technicians equally important but both rely on each other, in just the same way that Jesus said we are all part of one body. In fact, it is my experience that many musicians are excellent technicians and many operators have an intuitive understanding of good musicianship.

We are obviously surrounded by technology in every aspect of our lives and wherever innovation and technical equipment becomes an aid to effective worship, then it has a rightful place. The role, therefore, for the technician becomes increasingly important and God is calling to worship just as many keyboard operators as he does keyboard players; and anointing all to be effective in delivering the Word.

' ...now you are all the body of Christ , and each one of you is part of it...... If one part is honoured, every part rejoices with it.'
(1 Corinthians 12: 27, 26)

Brian Hillson
B & H Sound Services

107 Praise to Christ, the Lord incarnate

Words: Martin E. Leckebusch
Music & words adpt. Graham Kendrick

1. Praise to Christ, the Lord incarnate, gift of God by human birth: he it is who came among us, shared our life and showed our worth; ours the turmoil he encountered, ours the fight he made his own; now within our hearts his

Christ, the Man of Sorrows, tasting death for our release: his the cup of bitter anguish, ours the pardon, ours the peace; his the blood that seals forgiveness, ours the weight of guilt he bore so by death and resur-

Christ, the Priest eternal: still for us he intercedes; still he sees our pains and problems – how he understands our needs! Yesterday, today, forever, always he remains the same: pledged to bring us to the

This song is recorded on the Spring Harvest 2002 New Songs Album

Spi - rit makes his way of free - dom known.
rec - tion Christ has o - pened hea - ven's door.
Fa - ther, strong in grace and free from blame.

Chorus

Praise to Christ our Sa - viour and our King.

Praise to Christ our King.

2. Praise to
3. Praise to

King.

King.

108 Release my heart to worship

Jamie Hill

I am locked— a - way. Bring re - lease, all con-sum - ing fi - re, bring re -

lease,——— bring re - lease.—— *To repeat* C sus² *D.C.*

To end D sus⁴ D G

108a   The Lord God Almighty

Revelation 15: 3–4

'Great and marvellous are your deeds, Lord God Almighty.
Just and true are your ways, King of the ages.
Who will not fear you, O Lord,
and bring glory to your name?
For you alone are holy.
All nations will come and worship before you,
for your righteous acts have been revealed.'

109 Rock of ages

Words: A M Toplady (1740-1778)
Revised and adapted: Graham Kendrick
Melody: Graham Kendrick

231

110

Salvation, spring up
(Salvation)

Charlie Hall

With excitement

Salvation, spring up from the ground, Lord, rend the heav-ens and come down. Seek the lost and heal the lame; Je-sus bring glo-ry to your name. Let all the prod-i-gals run home, all of cre-a-tion waits and groans. Lord, we've heard of your great fame; Fa-ther, cause all to shout your name.

(Fine)

(continued over...)

we just weep____ and cry____ out to you.

110a   Walking in the light

**We go into the world
to walk in God's light,
to rejoice in God's love
and reflect God's glory.
Amen.**

From Methodist Worship Book 1999
Copyright © Trustees for Methodist Church Purposes.

111

Say the name of love

Graham Kendrick

1. Say the name of love:— Je-sus,— Je-sus.—
2. Say the name of wis-dom:— Je-sus,— Je-sus.—
3. Say the name of heal-ing:— Je-sus,— Je-sus.—

Say the name of peace:— Je-sus,— Je-sus.—
Name of re-ve - la-tion:— Je-sus,— Je-sus.—
Mi - ra-cles and won-ders:— Je-sus,— Je-sus.—

Say the name of mer - cy:— Je - sus,— Je - sus.—
Say the name of jus - tice:— Je - sus,— Je - sus.—
Say the name of po - wer:— Je - sus,— Je - sus.—

Last time (verse 3) to Coda

Say the name of good - ness:— Je - sus,— Je - sus.—
Par - don and for - give - ness:— Je - sus,— Je - sus.—
Here a - mong us now:— Je - sus,— Je - sus.—

(continued over...)

112   Shout with delight to the Lord

Words: D. A. Carson
Music: Steve James

1. Shout with de-light— to the Lord—— all you peo-ple, wor-ship the Lord—with full glad-ness of heart.— Come bow be-fore— him with songs full of prai-ses, joy-ful with all of your heart.— Know that the Lord,— he is—

2. En-ter his gates—with a song—— of thanks-giv-ing, en-ter his courts—with your tongue tuned to praise.— Our God is good,— and his love lasts for-e-ver; faith-ful-ness marks all his ways.—

God._____ Know that the Lord,____ he is__ God. For he made us,

we are his flock._____ The sheep of his pa - sture, and he is our Rock!

Know that the Lord,__ he is God!

God!

Know that the Lord,__he is God! Know that the Lord,__he is God!

113 Teach me of your ways
(Lord have your way)

Capo 2(G)
Steadily

David Gate

1. Teach me of your ways,
to hon - our you with all I have,
and that I learn to say: 'Not my will but yours,

2. Lord, I long to be
a faith - ful child who ho - nours you,
so Je - sus be in me, let your light shine through

114 Thank you, thank you for the blood

Rhythmically

Matt Redman

Thank you, thank you for the blood that you shed,___
Thank you, thank you for the bat-tle you won,___

stand-ing in its bles-sing we sing___ these free-dom songs.___
stand-ing in your vic-tory we sing___ sal-va-tion songs,

we sing___ sal-va-tion songs.___

Chorus

You have o-pened a way to the Fa-ther, where be-

fore we could ne-ver have come. Je-sus, count us as yours now for-

e-ver, as we sing___ these free-dom___ songs.___

We sing of all___ you've done,___ we

sing of all___ you've done,___ we sing of all___ you've___ done___

for us, won___ for us, paid___ for us. We ___ for us.___

115   The Lord is present here

Capo 3 (D)

Graham Kendrick

(continued over...)

glo - ry.　Ho-ly,　ho-ly, ho-ly Lord,——　God of pow'r and might,—— heav'n and

earth are full　　of your　glo - ry.'　(3. Let)

This song works well as a framework for words improvised in the flow of worship.
These are some more alternatives to choose from or add your own in the inspiration of the
moment.

We need to know you more, (x3)
Lord Jesus.

We need your power today, (x3)
Holy Spirit.

Your kindness overflows, (x3)
our Father.

This is a holy place, (x3)
come worship.

Because of your great love, (x3)
we worship.

We've come to seek your face, (x3)
Lord Jesus.

The Word and the Spirit – Together in Worship

I believe that one of our greatest challenges is to become worshippers who are rich in the Word and full of the Spirit, and the best reason for seeking this is because it is what we see in Jesus, the perfect worshipper.

The apostle Paul mentions psalms, hymns and spiritual songs in two different passages, Ephesians 5 and Colossians 3. On closer reading, several parallels stand out. For example, both chapters put psalms, hymns and spiritual songs right in the centre of nitty gritty life and relationship issues. Worship takes place in the flow of 'body' life. Now try placing the instructions immediately preceding each mention of psalms, hymns and spiritual songs side by side. Ephesians 5:18 instructs: 'Be filled with the Spirit. Speak to one another in psalms, hymns and spiritual songs. Sing and make music in your heart to the Lord.'

Colossians 3:16 instructs: 'Let the word of Christ dwell in you richly as you teach and admonish one another with all wisdom, as you sing psalms, hymns and spiritual songs with gratitude in your heart to God'. It seems the Word and the Spirit get equal billing! Worshippers can and should be simultaneously Spirit-filled and Word-enriched with the clear aim of edification, the building up of one another so that Christ is glorified in his body, the Church.

We are enjoying songs with plenty of motion, and rich emotion, and many of them have rich notion too. It's time, however, to recognise more than ever before that the Christian faith is established upon God's own revelation of himself in the person of Christ. This revelation is so rich and deep and broad and its doctrines so high and yet so earthy, practical and real, it deserves the best lyrical and theological skills we can muster.

We have received the greatest message the world will ever hear and songs remain one of the few ways by which believers memorise biblical material. Let's grasp this potential for teaching truth and guard it jealously for the sake of the One who is called the Truth.

And as we let the word of Christ dwell in us richly, and as we are filled with the Holy Spirit, and as we take these truths upon our lips in psalms and hymns and spiritual songs for the sake of building up one another in the faith, we will find an ever greater response rising from our hearts bringing pleasure to God.

Extracted and adapted from an article by Graham Kendrick, 'God and groove'

116 The Lord's my Shepherd
(Psalm 23)

Capo 1 (D)
Thoughtfully

Stuart Townend

2. He guides my ways in righteousness,
   and he anoints my head with oil,
   and my cup, it overflows with joy,
   I feast on his pure delights.

3. And though I walk the darkest path,
   I will not fear the evil one,
   for you are with me, and your rod and staff
   are the comfort I need to know.

117

The time has come
(Send revival)

Sara Harvey

(continued over...)

for your truth___ and for___ your word.___
that shines___ to all___ the world.___

If just one voice can make a diff-

'rence,___ if just one

pray'r can change the world,___

Fa - ther hear this cry___ that's al - ways on___ my heart,___

250

118
There is a green hill
in a far away country

Phil Baggaley, Dave Clifton
& Ian Blythe
Words adpt. from the hymn by C.F. Alexander

Steadily

1. There is a green hill in a far-a-way coun-try,
2. I may not know of the pain of his pas-sion,
3. So ve-ry dear-ly Je-sus has loved us,

it stands near a ci-ty, out-side a wall,
but I be-lieve that in my place he stood:
and all he would ask is that we love him too,

where Je-sus our Sa-viour, the King of all glo-ry
that I may know free-dom and live in for-give-ness,
and trust him for all that this life lays be-fore us,

suf-fered and died to save us all.
for I am re-deemed by his great love.
that we would try his work to do.

119   There is a hope so sure

Graham Kendrick

Slowly ♩ = 70

1. There is a hope so sure, a pro-mise so se-cure: the my-ste-ry of God at last made known. Trea-sures so vast ap-pear, all wis-dom, know-ledge here: it's Christ in us, the hope of glo-ry! And the life that I now live, no lon-ger

life so true, a life of love so pure, for all our sin a per-fect sa-cri-fice. And when that life was nailed, on cru-el cross im-paled, our sin-ful flesh with him was cru-ci-fied.

life so strong, that a whole world of wrong, and all the pow'rs of hell could not de-feat. For Je-sus rose a-gain, and if we died with him, with him we'll rise to share his end-less life.

This song is recorded on the Spring Harvest 2002 New Songs Album

is my own, Je-sus lives in me the hope of glo-ry. And each

day I live, no lon-ger is my own, Je-sus lives in me the hope of glo -

ry.

(Fine)

2. There is a
3. There is a

ry. And the life that

255

120

There's a lot of pain
(Outrageous grace)

Slowly

Godfrey Birtill

Verse

1. There's a lot of pain,— but a lot more heal - ing,
   lot of fear,— but a lot more free - dom;—
   there's a lot of trou - ble,— but a lot more peace.
   there's a lot of dark - ness,— but a lot more light.

There's a lot of hate,— but a lot more lov - ing,
There's a lot of cloud,— but a lot more vi - sion;—
there's a lot of sin,— but a lot more grace.—
there's a lot of pe - rish - ing,— but a lot more life.

Chorus

Oh, out - ra - geous grace!— Oh, out - ra - geous grace!— Love un -
Through my

This song is recorded on the **Spring Harvest 2001 Live Worship Album**

furled   by   hea - ven's   hand._____   Oh, out - stand._____

Je - sus   I   can

(D.C. 1st time only)   Mid section

2. There's   a

There's an   e - ne - my,_____   that seeks to__ kill__ what it can't con-

trol.   It   twists and turns_____   mak - ing moun - tains   out of   mole hills.

But I will   call on the Lord,_____   who is   wor - thy of   praise;_____   I

run to him   and I am   saved._____   Oh, out -

Coda

stand._____

257

121

This is the air I breathe
(Breathe)

Marie Barnett

This is— the air— I breathe, this is— the air—
This is— my dai - ly bread, this is— my dai-

— I breathe; your ho - ly pre - sence liv - ing in me.—
ly bread; your ve - ry word— spo - ken to me.—

And I,—

I'm des-perate for— you: and I,—

I'm lost with-out___ you.

121a   After Communion Prayer

Almighty God,
we thank you for feeding us
with the body and blood of your Son Jesus Christ.
Through him we offer you our souls and bodies
to be a living sacrifice.
Send us out in the power of your Spirit
to live and work to your praise and glory.
Amen.

From *Common Worship: Services and Prayers for the Church of England.*
Copyright © The Archbishops' Council 2000

122

Though trials will come
(Consider it joy)

♩ = 65

Graham Kendrick

1. Though trials will come, don't fear, don't run.
2. Though trials will come, won't fear, won't run.

Lift up your eyes, hold fast, be strong.
We'll lift up our eyes, hold fast, be strong.

Have faith, keep on be-liev - ing. Lift up your
Have faith, keep on be-liev - ing. We'll lift up our

eyes for God is at work in us,— mould-ing and
eyes for God is at
(verse 3) trust - ing him,— rea - dy for

Bridges to G

From D

From F

From B♭

From C

123 Together in this place of worship
(Emmanuel)

Raymond Badham

124   We are God's chosen holy nation
(Rising generation)

Dave Bankhead
& Mike Burn

Chorus: We are God's cho-sen ho-ly na-tion,— we be-long— to him a-lone,— and may this ris-ing ge-ne-ra-tion— wor-ship Christ— up-on his throne, wor-ship Christ— up-on his throne.

Verse:
1. We be-lieve— in God the Fa-ther, and in Christ, his pre-cious
2. We be-lieve— he sends his Spi-rit on us now, with gifts of

Son.   We be-lieve__ he died to save__ us,
pow'r: hear the Spi - rit call - ing out to us,

came to call__ us as his own.
where he leads us we will go.

We are God's

124a   Children of God

1 John 3: 1–3

How great is the love the Father has lavished on us, that we should be called children of God! And that is what we are! The reason the world does not know us is that it did not know him. Dear friends, now we are children of God, and what we will be has not yet been made known. But we know that when he appears, we shall be like him, for we shall see him as he is. Everyone who has this hope in him purifies himself, just as he is pure.

125   We fall down

Intensely

Chris Tomlin

126   We have come to seek you O God

A capella

♩ = 146

Anita Haigh

Part 1

We have come to seek you O God, just as we are we come.___

We have come to be sought by you, just as we are we come.___

1. — *2. - 5.*

We have We have come to seek you O God,

Part 2

1. Show us your mer-cy,

just as we are we come.___ We have come to be

O___ Lord, show us your face. Show

1. - 3. & D.C.

sought by you, just as we are we come.___ We have

us your mer-cy O___ Lord, show us your face.

Additional verses for part 2:

2. Teach us to listen O Lord,
   open our hearts. *x2*

3. In all our seeking O Lord,
   be our desire. *x2*

4. In all our speaking O Lord,
   be our true word. *x2*

127 We have come to a throne of grace
(King of grace)

Mark Altrogge

1. We have come to a throne of grace, where our migh-ty Sa-viour per-
2. We have come to a throne of grace, where our Prince of Peace ever

fects our praise; where wrath and judge-ment have been put a-way, where
lives, to pray for those his sa-cri-fice has bought and saved, where

not a trace of all our sin re-mains. You're the
saints and an-gels sing e-ter-nal praise.

King of grace un-end-ing; to your o-pen arms we run. You're the

King of grace—un - end - ing,— and we rest in your— un - fail -

- ing love,— and we rest in your— un - fail - ing—love.—

Last time

127a Blessing and Glory to God

Let us bless the Lord:
thanks be to God.
Blessing, honour and glory be yours,
here and everywhere,
now and forever. Amen.

From *Patterns for Worship.*
Copyright © The Central Board of Finance of The Church of England 1989, 1995; The Archbishops' Council 1999.

128   We lift our hands to worship you

Steve & Velveta Thompson

1. We lift our hands to worship you, we raise our
(2.) stand in awe be-fore you, we wor-ship

voice in praise. For you a-lone are
at your feet. Your ho-li-ness sur-

wor-thy: in ma-je-sty you reign.
rounds us, your beau-ty, Lord, we see.

We love you, a-dore you, we

bow down be-fore you. 2. We you.

128a God is our Refuge and Strength

From Psalm 46: 1–6 & 10–11

God is our refuge and strength
an ever-present help in trouble.
Therefore we will not fear, though the earth give way
and the mountains fall into the heart of the sea,
though its waters roar and foam
and the mountains quake with their surging.

There is a river whose streams make glad the city of God,
the holy place where the Most High dwells.
God is within her, she will not fall;
God will help her at break of day.

Nations are in uproar, kingdoms fall;
he lifts his voice, the earth melts.

'Be still, and know that I am God;
I will be exalted among the nations,
I will be exalted in the earth.'

The Lord Almighty is with us;
The God of Jacob is our fortress.

Joy Townhill

129

We stand united
(We are all one)

Dave Bankhead

1. We stand u-ni-ted in a love bought by his blood,
2. Just as the Fa-ther stands u-ni-ted with the Son,

one ho-ly na-tion and one ri-sen Lord,
though we are ma-ny, he has made us one.

and joined to-ge-ther o-ver-seas from shore to shore, we shall
In e-v'ry na-tion, that the world at last might see, we will

lift the name of Je-sus high once more. We are all one,
shout a-loud that Je-sus sets men free!

130   We've come to praise you

Kate Simmonds
& Stuart Townend

Capo 3 (D)
Gospel feel

We've come to praise you, 'cause you're wor - thy. No - bo - dy like you in your glo - ry. We love to praise you, 'cause you're ho - ly, awe - some, won - der - ful, migh - ty God.

And e - v'ry - thing that you do comes from a heart of love and a hand of mer - cy; for you are faith - ful and true, work - ing all things

131 What astonishing mercy and power
(To the praise of his glorious grace)

Words: D.A. Carson
Music: Paul Boling
& Gerald Edmonds

Steadily

1. What a - sto - nish - ing mer - cy and pow'r:_____ in ac -
2. With de - spi - ca - ble self - love and rage,_____ we re -
3. Pro - vi - den - tial - ly rul - ing all things_____ to con -
4. Long be - fore the cre - a - tion be - gan,_____ he fore -
5. We were blessed in the hea - ven - ly realms_____ long be -

cord with__ his plea - sure and will._____ He cre - a - ted each
belled and__ fell un - der the curse._____ Yet__ God did not
form to__ the end he de - signed,_____ he my - ster - ious - ly
knew those__ he'd ran - som in Christ;_____ long be - fore time's cold
fore be - ing in - clu - ded in Christ._____ Since we heard the good

pla - net, each flow'r,_____ ev - 'ry gal - ax - y, mi - crobe and
rip out the page_____ and de - stroy all who love the per -
go - verns, and brings_____ his e - ter - nal wise plans in - to
hour - glass ran,_____ he or - dained the su - preme sa - cri -
news, o - ver - whelmed,_____ we reach for - ward to seize Pa - ra -

hill;_____ he sus - pen - ded this pla - net in space,_____ to the
verse._____ No, he chose us to make a new race,_____ to the
time._____ He works out ev - 'ry step, ev - 'ry trace,_____ to the
fice._____ In the cross he re - moved our dis - grace,_____ to the
dise._____ We shall see him our - selves, face to face,_____ to the

praise of his glo - ri - ous grace. To the praise of his glo - ri - ous
praise of his glo - ri - ous grace. To the praise of his glo - ri - ous
praise of his glo - ri - ous grace. To the praise of his glo - ri - ous
praise of his glo - ri - ous grace. To the praise of his glo - ri - ous
praise of his glo - ri - ous grace. To the praise of his glo - ri - ous

grace,_____ to the praise of his glo - ri - ous grace._____
grace,_____ to the praise of his glo - ri - ous grace._____
grace,_____ to the praise of his glo - ri - ous grace._____
grace,_____ to the praise of his glo - ri - ous grace._____
grace,_____ to the praise of his glo - ri - ous grace._____

132   What can I say?

Capo 3(D)
Steadily

Neil Bennetts

What can I say, but 'I love you'? What can I
do, but to bow down? What can I

say, but 'I praise you'? As the train of your robe fills this tem-
do, but to wor - ship? On - ly you are the One who is wor-

1. ple, as the sound of your voice fills this place. What can I
thy, on - ly

2. you are the One who is Lord. **Chorus** Great is the Lord, so great is the Lord,

Dm(Bm) Dm⁷(Bm) Gm(Em) Csus⁴(A) B♭/D(G) C/E(A)

right-eous and true___ God, ho-ly and pure.___ I fall on my knees,___

F(D) A(F♯) Dm(Bm) Dm⁷(Bm) Gm⁷(Em) B♭/C(G) C⁷(A) F(D)

con-fess-ing my need___ for more of your pre - sence, Lord.___

132a   The Lord Reigns
Psalm 99: 1–5

The Lord reigns,
    let the nations tremble;
he sits enthroned between the cherubim,
    let the earth shake.
Great is the Lord in Zion;
    he is exalted over all the nations.
Let them praise your great and awesome name –
    he is holy.

The King is mighty, he loves justice –
    you have established equity;
in Jacob you have done
    what is just and right.
Exalt the Lord our God
    and worship at his footstool; he is holy.

133 What to say, Lord?
(Every day)

With life

Joel Houston

1. What to say,— Lord? It's you who gave— me life, and I
2. E - v'ry day,— Lord, I'll learn to stand— up-on— your word,—

— can't ex-plain— just how much you mean— to me— now
— and I pray— that I, that I may come— to know— you more;—

that you have saved— me, Lord. I give all that— I am— to you,—
that you would guide— me in e-v'ry sin - gle step— I take,— that

— that e-v'ry day— I can be a light— that shines—your name.
e-v'ry day— I can be your light— un - to——the world.—

283

134

When I survey
(Celtic version)

With a slow lilt

Words. Issac Watts
Music. Trad
Arr. Dave Bainbridge, Joanne Hogg
& Terl Bryant

1. When I sur - vey   the wond - rous cross   on which the Prince   of Glo - ry died,   my rich - est gain   I count but loss   and pour con - tempt   on all my pride.

2. For - bid it, Lord,   that I should boast   save in the death   of Christ my God: all the vain things   that charm me most,   I sa - cri - fice   them to his blood.

3. See from his head,   his hands, his feet,   sor - row and love   flow min - gled down: did e'er such love   and sor - row meet,   or thorns com - pose   so rich a crown?

4. Were the whole realm   of na - ture mine,   that were an of - f'ring far too small;   love so a - maz - ing, so di - vine,   de - mands my soul,   my life, my all!

135

Capo 3 (D)

Gospel feel

When I was lost
(There is a new song)

Kate & Miles Simmonds

(continued over...)

This song is recorded on the Spring Harvest 2002 New Songs Album

in my mouth,___ there is a deep cry
on this Rock,___ my life is - hid - den now with

in my heart,___ a hymn of praise to Al - migh - ty God,___ hal - le - lu -
Christ in God.___ The old has gone and the new has come,___ hal - le - lu -

jah!___ And now I
jah!___ Your love has lif - ted

me.

me. Ma - ny are___ the won - ders you___ have done,___

136 Worship the Lord

shout a - loud___ your praise.___ De - clare his glo - ry a-
put their hope___ in God.___
tell of all___ you've done.___

mong all___ the na - tions. De - clare his ma - je-sty, his

splen - dour___ and___ pow'r.___ Pro - claim sal - va - tion, his

good - ness___ and mer - cy; for great is the Lord___ and___ most

wor - thy,___ wor - thy___ of praise.

Yet will I praise him

From Habakkuk 3

Geraldine Latty

1. 'Tho the fig tree doesn't blossom and no
2. When the night is over-whelming and the
3. Be the strength, Lord, in my weakness, let your

ri-pened grapes appear, 'tho the harvest fails and fields provide no food;
day is far from clear, when my heart is restless for the peace of God;
song be in my night; be my rock when all around is sinking sand.

I'll be joy-ful in my Saviour, the
let your song, Lord, through the ages, through the
Be the light, Lord, in my darkness, be the

Lord who is my strength; he will keep my ways and lead me in his truth.
pro-phets you have giv'n; lift my mind and heart to gaze upon you, Lord.
vi-sion of my eyes: in my pas-sing days you are the great 'I Am'.

291

138 You are God in heaven
(Let my words be few)

Steadily

Matt & Beth Redman

You are God in hea - ven,___ and here___ am I___ on earth;___
The sim-plest of all love___ songs___ I want___ to bring___ to you;___

so I'll let___ my words___ be few:___ Je-
so I'll let___ my words___ be few:___ Je-

sus, I___ am so___ in love___ with you.___ And I'll
sus, I___ am so___ in love___ with you.___

stand in awe___ of you,___ yes, I'll

stand in awe___ of you.___ And I'll

This song is recorded on the Spring Harvest 2001 Live Worship Album

let my words— be few:— Je - sus, I— am so— in love— with you.—

To repeat
To end
Fine

138a **Prayer based on Revelation 8: 1**

Your purpose, Lord God, silences heaven.
Forgive our empty chatter,
our mindless gossip in your presence.
Keep us silent before you.

Your purpose, Lord God, silences heaven.
How awesome is your justice,
how great your victory!
Keep us silent before you.

Your purpose, Lord God, silences heaven.
Angels and archangels await your bidding,
cherubim and seraphim stand on your summons.
Keep us silent before you.

Paul Sheppy

139 You are holy

li - ness._____
_ are with us._____
_ are with us._____

You are ho - ly,___ you are God._

139a   Meditation on John 13: 1–17

When John came to write about that last supper
he didn't think about the bread and the wine – Jesus' death.
He remembered Jesus' love.

He watched closely as his friend got up from the meal,
and wrapped a towel round his waist;
he stared amazed as he poured water into a bowl
and was in awe at what happened next:

'He washed my feet,
the Master washed my feet.'

And when he tried to make sense of it later,
tried to understand what it all meant,
he came to one conclusion
it was, 'to show the full extent of his love.'

Joy Townhill

140

You are my anchor

With a steady rock feel

Stuart Townend

1. You are my an - chor,— my light and my sal - va - tion.
(2.) — Lord,— make straight the path be - fore— me.

You are my re - fuge,— my heart will not fear.—
Do not for-sake— me,— my hope is in you.—

Though my foes— sur - round— me on ev - 'ry hand,— they will stum-
As I walk— through life,— I am con - fi - dent— I will see—

ble and fall— while in grace— I stand.— In my day— of trou - ble, you hide—
—your good-ness— with e - ve - ry step,— and my heart— di - rects— me to seek—

This song is recorded on the Spring Harvest 2002 New Songs Album

me and set me a-bove
to sing this song of love:

you in all that I do,
so I will wait for you.

Chorus
One thing I will ask of you, this will I pray: to dwell in your house,

O Lord, e-ve-ry day; to gaze u-pon your love - ly face,

and rest in the Fa - ther's em-brace.

(Fine)

D.C. al fine

2. Teach me your way,

141 You are the Sovereign 'I Am'
(Your name is holy)

Brian Doerksen

142

You are the stone
(No one like you, Lord)

Robin Mark

1. You are the stone___ that the buil- ders re- jec- - ted,
2. When from the cross___ you to the depths de- scend- - ed,
3. Then from the earth you to the heights a - scend- - ed,

a rock of re- fuge where my pride is bro- ken,___
the hosts of hell con- spired to make you cap- tive,___
where you are seat- ed at your Fa- ther's right___ hand,

a sure foun - da - tion when the sand is sink - ing,___
but e - v'ry chain of sin and death you've bro - ken,___
for - e - ver plead - ing for the souls you've cap - tured,

where we are built up- on___ like liv- ing___ stones.
and tri- umphed o - ver by___ your migh- ty___ pow'r. There is
for - e - ver watch- ing as___ you call us___ home.

This song is recorded on the Spring Harvest 2002 New Songs Album

no one else like you, there is no one like you, Lord; there is

no one else like you, Son of Man and Son of God, Son of Man

Last time to Coda ⊕   *Last time D.S.*

1.
D/G   C/G

2.   *Bridge*

and Son of God. *(Last time only)* (There is)

I want to run

the race you've set be - fore me, e - ven to share

in the suf-f'ring of the cross, that I might

(continued over...)

143 You came to earth
(I surrender)

Andrew Grinnell

(continued over...)

here you showed＿ me the love and mer - cy I need＿
heart's re - spond - ing to your in - vi - ta - tion to come,＿
lose my - self＿ I am found in you,＿ Lord, for you＿
shown me ser - vice, taught me how to fol - low, now yours＿
crease the fire＿ that burns with - in＿ me for more＿
give you praise,＿ you are all I wor - ship, you're Lord

1.
in my life.＿ You＿
'Fol - low me'.＿
have my life.＿ You＿
I will be.＿
of your love.＿ The＿
of my life.＿

2.   *Chorus*
I sur -

ren - der my life＿ to you, Je - sus,＿ I am
heard how you called,＿ 'Come and fol - low';＿ you can

want - ing to fol - low your call.＿ You are teach - ing me more＿ of the ways＿
lead me wher - e - ver you will.＿ And I'm liv - ing to see＿ all you've pro -

that you want me to live.
mised for me is ful-filled.
I have

2. The
3. For-

And I'm

liv-ing to see all you've pro - mised for me is ful-filled.

And I'm liv-ing to see all you've pro - mised for me is ful-filled.

144 You hear, O Lord

Graham Kendrick

(continued over...)

145 You pour out grace

Steadily

Gareth Robinson
& Joannah Oyeniran

1. You pour out grace on the bro - ken - heart - ed, and
2. You de - mon - stra - ted the life of love to me,

you lift the hope of the wea - ry soul, and you
and how it was that you wan - ted me to live.

stretch out your hand with your lov - ing mer - cy.
Heart of com - pas - sion and hands of heal - ing:

You saw this heart that was lost and bro - ken, and
I need your Spi - rit to help ac - com - plish this.

(continued over...)

you felt the pain of my lone - li - ness,— and you
A - bun - dant grace and your strength—— in weak - ness,

be - friend - ed me and re - stored—— my dig - ni - ty.——
the stea - dy hand of the Fa - ther hold - ing me.——

Chorus

You———— a - lone——— re - vealed—— the love— of God—

— to me,— and you———— a - lone——— have giv - en ev - 'ry - thing—

— for me;— and you———— a - lone——— de - serve—— the high - est praise,—

146

You shaped the heavens
(Maker of all things)

Jer 10:16, Col 1:16-17,
Ps 19:1

Tim Hughes

Strongly

1. You shaped the hea-vens and the earth, re-vealed your splen-dour. You spoke your life in-to our hearts, so we be-long to you. You are the mak-er of all things, First and the Last, cre-a-tion sings praise

2. Cre-a-tor God, in you all things now hold to-ge-ther. Work-ing your won-ders day by day, you'll reign for-e - ver.

to you, God.⸺ You're reign - ing⸺ in glo-ry,⸺ An-cient⸺ of Days,⸺ your peo-ple⸺ sing praise⸺ to⸺ you, God.⸺

1.3. (Fine) *2.* And earth joins⸺ with hea - ven,⸺ de-clar - ing⸺ your glo - ry;⸺ pro - claim - ing⸺ the works of⸺ your⸺ hands.⸺

D.S. al fine

2. Yes, works of⸺ your⸺ hands.⸺ You are the

147

Your face outshines
(King of glory)

Matt Redman
& David Gate

With strength

1. Your

face—— out - shines—— the bright - est sun,
eyes—— that blaze—— like burn - ing fire,

Je - sus, you're

2. voice—like rush - ing wa - ters sounds,
in—your hands—— you hold the stars,

Je - sus—you're

glor - i - ous, you—are— so glor - i - ous.——

With

po - wer - ful, you—are— so po - wer - ful.——

And

148

Your kindness

James Gregory

♩ = 136

1. Your kind-ness o-ver-whelmed me, the love that cap-tured me. You helped me to be-lieve that you de-light in me.
You led me to the Fa-ther, and in-tro-duced us there, the Spi-rit poured out grace, and filled me with your praise.

2. Your plans for me are great-er than I had e-ver thought, you're dai-ly chang-ing me, re-veal-ing more to me.
My love for you is grow-ing, and as I reach for you; your Spi-rit pours out grace and fills me with your praise.

(1st & 3rd times) **Chorus**

You are won-der-ful, beau-ti-ful, mer-ci-ful, and all my life and my heart

be-longs— to you. You are won — be-longs— to you.

148a   I believe

Prayer on the wall of a prison cell in Cologne written by a Jew awaiting persecution or death:

I believe in the sun even when it is not shining.
I believe in love even when I cannot feel it.
I believe in God when he is silent.

Source: traditional

149   Your love is amazing
(Hallelujah)

Brian Doerksen
& Brenton Brown

1.(3.) Your love is— a-maz - ing, stea-dy and—un-chang - ing; your love is— a moun-
  (2.) - sing, I can feel— it ris - ing, all the joy—that's grow-

- tain, firm be-neath— my feet.___ Your love is— a mys-
ing deep in-side— of me.___ E- v'ry time— I see

t'ry, how you gent - ly lift___ me; when I am— sur-round -
- you, all your good - ness shines___ through, I can feel— this God—

ed, your love car - ries me.
- song ris-ing up— in me.

Hal-le-lu - jah, hal-le-lu-

This song is recorded on the Spring Harvest 2001 New Songs Album

jah, hal-le-lu-jah, your love makes— me sing. Hal-le-lu-

jah, hal-le-lu-jah, hal-le-lu-jah,

Last time to Coda ⊕ *1.2.* *D.C.*

your love makes— me sing.

2. Your love is— sur-pri
3. Your love is— a-maz

3.

Yes, you make— me— sing, Lord, you make— me—

D.S. al Coda

— sing, sing,— sing, how you make— me— sing. Hal-le-lu

(continued over...)

⊕ *Coda*

Lord, you make me sing,

how you make me sing.

149a   Come let us sing

Leader: Come let us sing
All: **Come let us sing**
Leader: Come let us praise
All: **Come let us praise**
Leader: Come let us rejoice
All: **Come let us rejoice**
Leader: The Saviour reigns
All: **The Saviour reigns**

Jesus is worthy   **(Jesus...)**
The Lamb who was slain   **(The Lamb...)**
To receive glory   **(To receive...)**
Honour and praise   **(Honour and praise...)**

Our God is good   **(Our God...)**
Our God is great   **(Our God...)**
We declare to the world   **(We declare...)**
That our God saves   **(That our God...)**

Each line is spoken by the leader and echoed by the congregation, then the four line verse [ie just the leader lines] are repeated with leader and congregation together. The complete praise shout will work over an instrumental chorus.

Geraldine Latty

All-age Worship

Matthew 21 retells the event when the children were shouting in the temple area 'Hosanna to the Son of David', the chief priests were indignant and Jesus replied, "have you never read, 'from the lips of children and infants, you have ordained praise'?"

- It is vital to have a positive vision and appreciation of the importance of adults and children worshipping together, learning from each other.
- Children need to be nurtured and taught how to praise and worship so always have an inclusive approach and good explanations.
- Worship needs to be central, holding the whole service together. The theme needs to come through clearly in the worship and praise.
- Avoid long sections of worship and praise, instead have frequent short sections throughout the meeting.
- Use a mix of adult songs but ensure the lyrics are simple and children friendly. Sometimes use the first verse and chorus of a long song and repeat.
- To engage the pre-school age group a couple of 'children's songs' with actions are helpful.
- Use familiar songs and only aim to teach one new song if appropriate.
- Variety is key: energetic and fun along with quiet worshipful and reflective. However, try to avoid quick drastic changes, eg lively dancing song followed by a still reflective prayer. It is important to manage the energy of the all age congregation.
- Involve children in reading liturgical texts and scripture. These can be inserted into songs, with the music continuing quietly in the background, underneath the spoken word.
- Echo prayers are very good for the younger members.
- Visuals are vital – use symbols, pictures and props to visualise the theme of the song, scripture text or prayer.
- Worship participation with flags and ribbons helps engage the children. Smaller ribbons can be made for the children to participate. Try short lengths of ribbon attached to shower curtain rings.
- Small musical shakers are great for young children who cannot read the words of the songs but can worship through movement and music!
- Any participative sections need wise planning and management so as to avoid a free for all.

I believe God loves to see and 'dwell' in the hearts of young and old in praise and worship, so all the time consuming preparation is worth it.

Rachael Orrell
Spring Harvest Leadership Team

150 Your name

Andrew Bromley

1. Your name,___ stron-ger than___ I know, the
(2.)___ all cre-a-tion knows,___ the
(3.)___ high-er than___ them all;___

deep-er than___ a thou-sand words___ could say,___ your name.___
One who gave___ it life___ with breath a-lone,___ your name.___
Ho-ly One___ of God,___ the Lord___ of lords,___ your name.___

Your name,___ fire___ in___ my soul,___
Your name,___ glo-ry now___ dis-played:___
Your name,___ hea-ven's on-ly Son,___

heal-ing for___ a hurt-ing heart___ to-day,___ your name.___
all the earth___ be-longs___ to you___ a-lone,___ your name,___ your
high and lif-ted up___ for e-ver-more,___ your name,___ your

Thematic Index
Numbers refer to songs, not pages

Thematic Index (cont'd)

Proclamation (cont'd)

Renewal and Refreshment

Response

Spiritual Warfare

Suffering and Trials

Suitable for solo or presentation

Unity

Spring Harvest 2002 Theme

Scripture Index

Scripture Index (cont'd)

Guitar Chords

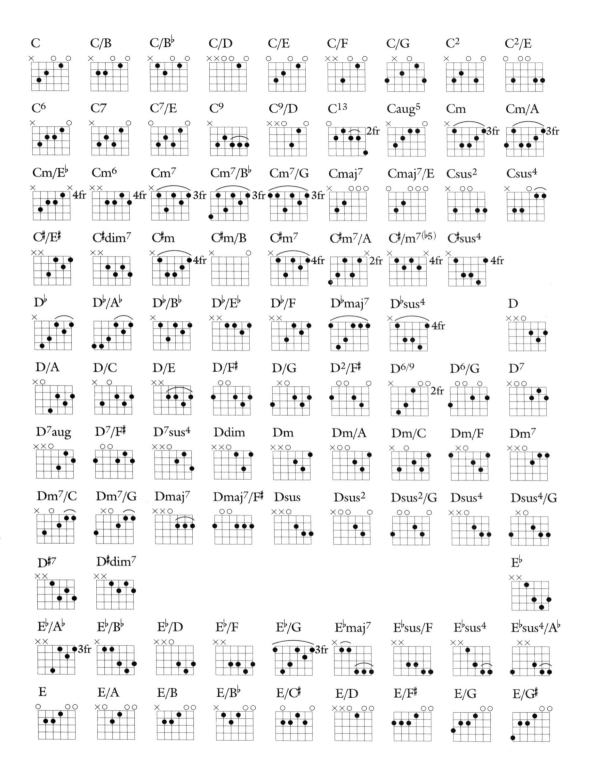

Guitar Chords

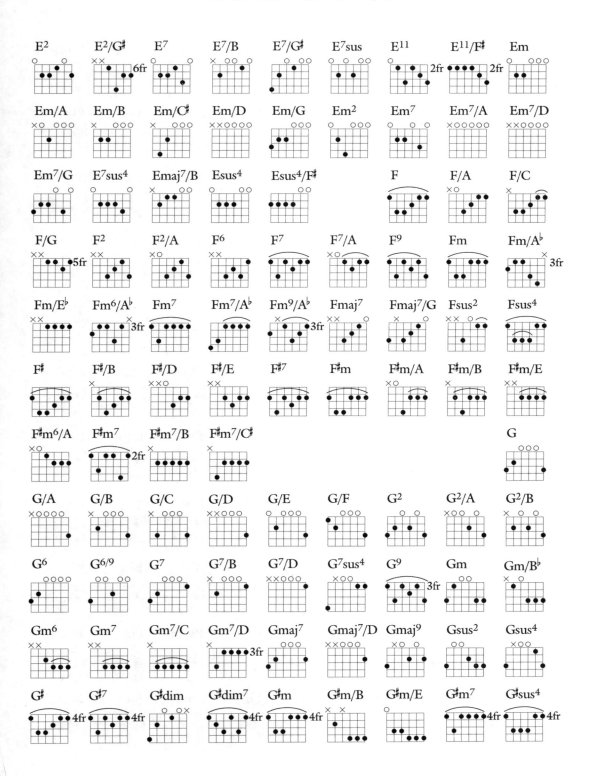

Guitar Chords

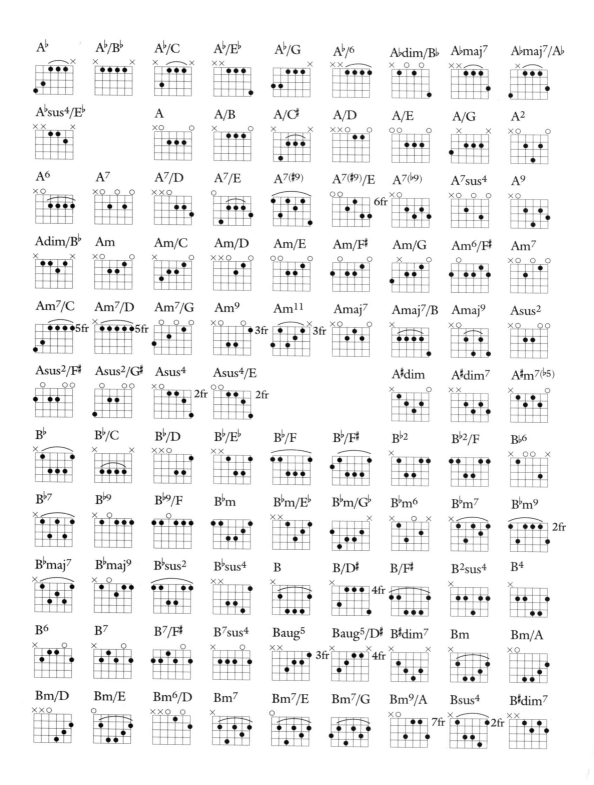

Index of Liturgy and Prayers

Index of Bible Verses

Worship Today

Worship Today is a new and unique resource that brings together the most popular songs and hymns being sung in the UK church today.

"At last, all the songs we're singing in one book ... "

Worship Today gives you:

- The top 500 songs and hymns – compiled using CCLI data Oct 1999–March 2000
- A versatile resource – encompassing traditional hymns, old favourites and contemporary songs
- New layout – larger pages, fewer page turns
- Practical indexing – Thematic, Scripture, Alphabetical and keys
- Quality binding that lies flat on a music stand
- Liturgy, prayers and Scripture – to enrich your congregational worship
- Complete church resource – hardback words edition also available
- Permission to photocopy – CCLI's MRL licence holders can photocopy within the terms of their licence

Details – including a complete song listing – are available at www.worshiptoday.co.uk or phone Spring Harvest on 01825 769000.

Worship Today is published by Spring Harvest

Christian Copyright Licensing (Europe) Ltd has its finger on the pulse of hymn and song usage in the UK. This compilation draws on data from CCLE's 18,000 church licence holders for the period October 1999 to March 2000.